SFPE Engineering Guide to Performance-Based Fire Protection

SFPE Engineering Guide to Performance-Based Fire Protection

Society of Fire Protection Engineers

 **National Fire Protection Association**
Quincy, MA

 Society of Fire Protection Engineers
Bethesda, MD

Product Manager: Brad Gray
Developmental Editor: Betsey Henkels
Editorial-Production Services: Publishers' Design and Production Services, Inc.
Cover Design: Greenwood Associates
Manufacturing Manager: Ellen Glisker
Printer: Victor Graphics, Inc.

 National Fire Protection Association, Inc.
One Batterymarch Park
Quincy, Massachusetts 02169-7471

 Society of Fire Protection Engineers
7315 Wisconsin Ave., Suite 620E
Bethesda, Maryland 20814

NFPA No.: SFPE06
ISBN-10: 0-87765-789-0
ISBN-13: 978-087765-789-7
Library of Congress Control No.: 2006934696

Printed in the United States of America
07   08   09   10   11   5   4   3   2   1

SFPE Task Group on Performance-Based Analysis and Design

CHAIRMAN

Eric R. Rosenbaum, P.E., FSFPE
Hughes Associates, Inc.

MEMBERS

John F. Bender, P.E., FSFPE
Office of the Maryland State
Fire Marshal

Craig Beyler, Ph.D., FSFPE
Hughes Associates, Inc.

Allan Coutts,
P.E., Ph.D., FSFPE
Washington Safety
Management Solutions

Richard Custer, FSFPE
ARUP Fire Engineering

John Devlin, P.E.
Schirmer Engineering
Corporation

Joshua M. Fleischer
Framatome ANP

Daniel Gemeny, P.E.
Rolf Jensen & Associates Inc.

Cynthia Gier, P.E.
CMG Fire Protection
Engineering, Inc.

George Hadjisophocleous,
P.Eng., Ph.D., FSFPE
Carleton University

Wayne D. Holmes,
P.E., FSFPE
HSB Professional Loss
Control

Howard Hopper, P.E.
Underwriters Laboratories Inc.

Roland J. Huggins, P.E.
American Fire Sprinkler
Association

Ian MacDonald
R.J. Bartlett Engineering Ltd.

Christopher Marrion,
P.E., FSFPE
ARUP Fire Engineering

Brian M. McGraw, P.E.
Total Fire Solutions

Anthony Militello, P.E.
Naval Facilities Engineering
Command

Frederick W. Mowrer,
P.E., Ph.D., FSFPE
University of Maryland

Bijan Najafi, P.E.
Science Applications
International Corp.

Daniel J. O'Connor,
P.E., FSFPE
Schirmer Engineering
Corporation

Michael O'Hara,
P.E., FSFPE
The MountainStar Group, Inc.

Igor Oleszkiewicz, P.Eng.
National Research Council
of Canada

Milosh Puchovsky, P.E.
National Fire Protection
Association

Jeffrey Shapiro,
P.E., FSFPE
International Code
Consultants

Amal Tamim
Warrington Fire Research

Andrew Valente, P.E.
ARUP Fire Engineering

John Watts Jr.,
Ph.D., FSFPE
Fire Safety Institute

Christopher Wood, J.D.
ARUP Fire Engineering

STAFF

Morgan J. Hurley, P.E.
Society of Fire Protection Engineers

Contents

11 Developing a Fire Protection Engineering Design Brief   129

12 Documentation and Specifications   137

13 Managing Facility Changes   149

Appendices

A Additional Readings   151

Preface

The *SFPE Engineering Guide to Performance-Based Fire Protection Analysis and Design of Buildings* was first published in 2000. The guide was developed by the Society of Fire Protection Engineers for engineers in recognition of the increased acceptance of performance-based design. Prior to the publication of the guide, performance-based design was generally practiced on an ad hoc basis, in which the design process was determined by the engineer performing the design in consultation with project stakeholders. While this guide provides a process for performance-based design, it also recognizes that each performance-based design is different, and, therefore, the process is intended to be flexible.

Performance-based codes and design methods from several countries, including Australia, New Zealand, the United Kingdom, and the Nordic countries, were consulted in developing the first edition of this guide. However, since publication of the first edition, several new performance-based codes have been published, and additional experience has been gained. The guide has been revised based on this new information.

The *SFPE Code Official's Guide to Performance Based Design Review* has also been published since the original publication of this guide. The *Code Official's Guide* was published to facilitate review of designs and identification of items that should be considered when reviewing a performance-based design.

In addition, SFPE has published several other guides to assist in the engineering aspects of a performance-based analysis. These guides include the following:

- *Assessing Flame Radiation to External Targets from Pool Fires*
- *Predicting 1st and 2nd Degree Skin Burns from Thermal Radiation*
- *Piloted Ignition of Solid Materials under Radiant Exposure*
- *Evaluation of the Computer Fire Model DETACT-QS*
- *Fire Exposures to Structural Elements*
- *Human Behavior in Fire*

CHAPTER 1

Introduction

1.1 Purpose

1.1.1 General The *SFPE Engineering Guide to Performance-Based Fire Protection* outlines a process for using a performance-based approach in the design and assessment of building fire safety within both prescriptive and performance-based code systems. It is intended that this guide serve as a resource in the pursuit of a building or fire regulation's performance-based design option or in the development of an equivalent means of protection to prescriptive code requirements. This guide can also serve as a stand-alone resource in which no building or fire regulations are applicable or in which protection above and beyond that specified by building and fire regulations is desired.

1.1.2 Intent The intent of the guide is to provide the following:

- A process by which engineers can develop fire protection measures that provide levels of safety, deemed acceptable by the stakeholders, without imposing unnecessary constraints on other aspects of building design and operation
- Guidance that can be used by both qualified engineers and authorities having jurisdiction as a means to determine and document that specific fire safety goals are achieved for specific fire hazards for a particular project
- Parameters that should be considered in performance-based analysis or design

1.2 Fundamentals

1.2.1 Audience   The guide is written for engineers practicing fire protection engineering who are developing and evaluating analyses and designs. Such engineers are qualified by education, training, and experience and have the following characteristics:

- Possess a working knowledge of applicable building and fire regulations
- Are competent in the application of scientific and engineering principles for protecting people, their environment, and their property from unwanted consequences of fires
- Possess a working knowledge of the nature and characteristics of fire and related hazards, as well as how fires originate, develop, and spread
- Understand fire hazards and risk
- Understand fire prevention and building systems used to protect against fire effects
- Understand the impact of fire and fire effluents on buildings, processes, systems, and people
- Possess competence regarding the behavior of building occupants and emergency responders during emergency situations
- Practice with ethical engineering responsibility

Unless otherwise noted, the term *engineer*, when referenced in this guide, means the engineer practicing fire protection engineering who is responsible for the performance-based analysis and design. It is the responsibility of the engineer and design team to possess the required knowledge and skills necessary to perform the performance-based design, analysis, and verification and to document that information about the design team to the authority having jurisdiction and the client.

1.2.2 Evaluation of Safety Parameters   Factors and fire safety parameters addressed in this guide need to be considered when conducting a performance-based design. The factors and parameters to be evaluated or addressed depend on the context of the analysis and the reasons for undertaking the design. Not all factors and parameters within this guide are necessarily key considerations for every design, but they should all be accounted for with substantiation provided as to why some factors and parameters are insignificant.

1.2.3 Documentation
When undertaken, the process and methodology described in this guide require documentation. This guide delineates the information gathered and employed during each step of the process as a means of establishing conclusions and recommendations incorporated in the written documents.

1.2.4 Engineering Responsibilities
The role of the engineer on a project that involves performance-based design can include the following responsibilities:

- Ascertain stakeholder goals and objectives
- Identify and inform the stakeholders of fire hazards and risks
- Identify regulatory compliance issues
- Establish and execute the performance-based analysis
- Make fire safety recommendations that are consistent with stakeholder objectives and regulatory requirements
- Secure acceptance by the stakeholders, including authorities having jurisdiction, of the proposed performance-based design
- Verify the implementation of the performance-based design via construction document development and field observations
- Develop an operations and maintenance (O&M) manual that outlines the design conditions that must be satisfied to ensure continued acceptability of the design over the life of the building

1.2.5 Stakeholder Roles
The engineer and other stakeholders must understand the engineer's role in the project and how the engineer fits into the project delivery process and design team structure.

1.2.6 Conflicts of Interest
The engineer and other stakeholders should understand the potential conflicts of interest that may arise in performance-based fire safety design and should take appropriate actions to either avoid conflicts of interest or manage unavoidable conflicts of interest. Examples of situations in which potential conflicts of interest may arise include the following:

1. Situations in which the engineer is solely responsible for selecting the design objectives or performance criteria as well as the design fire scenarios
2. Situations in which the engineer is serving as a peer reviewer on other projects involving the client or other stakeholders

3. Situations in which a peer reviewer is serving as the engineer on other projects involving the client or other stakeholders

4. Situations in which the engineer or peer reviewer has a business or personal relationship with a manufacturer, vendor, or other entity that might influence the engineer's or peer reviewer's objectivity or decision-making capabilities

There are also other situations in which conflicts of interest may arise.

1.2.7 Implementation For efficient implementation, it is recommended that the performance-based process start in the concept development, feasibility, or planning stages of a project. However, this methodology can be used anytime during the design and construction of a building.

1.3 Scope

1.3.1 This guide provides a process for the application of scientific and engineering principles to the protection of people and property from the unwanted effects of fire. It provides a process for undertaking a performance-based fire protection engineering approach to building fire safety analysis and design, and it provides a means of assessing the effectiveness of the total building fire protection system in achieving specified fire and life safety objectives.

1.3.2 This guide presents a process for performance-based fire protection engineering for buildings. However, this design guide might be used for other applications, when justified by an engineer. Possible other applications include the performance design of buildings or facilities based on the exposure from other hazards or risks, such as explosions or toxic chemical releases.

1.3.3 This guide defines the performance-based process and provides references to available sources of fire protection engineering analysis and design tools and methods, fire test methods and data, performance criteria, and other pertinent information. However, this guide does not provide specific fire protection engineering analysis and design tools, methods, or data, nor does this guide provide specific performance, acceptance, or design criteria for use in the analysis and design process. However, some specific tools, methods, and criteria are provided for the purpose of serving as explanatory examples. The information cited in the examples does not necessarily constitute the correct or only information pertinent to a specific design project. (See 1.5.6.)

1.3.4 This guide outlines procedures and a methodology for undertaking building fire safety designs and is intended for use by engineers. It does not detail all the engineering technology required for building fire safety design.

1.4 Use and Application

1.4.1 Performance-based design of fire protection systems may offer a number of advantages over prescriptive-based design. Some of the advantages of performance-based design include the following:

1. Specifically addresses a building's unique aspects or uses, as well as specific stakeholder needs, and considers those of the broader community where appropriate.

2. Provides a basis for development and selection of alternative fire protection options based on the project's needs (e.g., in the case that the code-prescribed solution does not meet the stakeholders' needs).

3. Allows the safety levels provided by alternative design options to be compared. Comparing options provides a mechanism to determine what level of safety, at what cost, is acceptable.

4. Requires the use of a variety of tools in the analysis, bringing increased engineering rigor and resulting in innovative design options.

5. Results in a fire protection strategy in which fire protection systems are integrated, rather than designed in isolation.

A comprehensive performance-based engineering approach may provide more effective fire protection to address a specific need, in addition to improved knowledge of the loss potential.

1.4.2 Tools of performance-based fire protection engineering might include deterministic analysis, probabilistic analysis techniques, application of the theory of the fire dynamics, application of deterministic and probabilistic fire effects modeling, and application of human behavior and toxic effects modeling.

1.4.3 Engineers have a duty to hold paramount the safety, health, and welfare of the public, while at the same time acting as faithful agents or trustees for each employer or client they serve. There could be tension between these competing duties for engineers engaged in performance- or prescriptive-based fire protection analysis and design. In order to manage the possible tensions that might arise between private interests and public welfare in performance-based fire protection analysis and design, as well as to promote more uniform application of performance-based fire safety design concepts and methods, potential conflicts of interest should be recognized and managed through the use and application of this guide.

1.4.4   The use and application of this guide can be applied through a building or fire regulation's performance-based design option or in the development of an equivalent means of protection to a prescriptive code's requirements. This guide can also be applied where no building or fire regulations are applicable or where protection above and beyond that specified by building and fire regulations is desired.

1.4.5   The application of performance-based design is often applied through the equivalency provision found in many building and fire regulations. Equivalency offers an alternative means of providing an equivalent or greater degree of safety than that prescribed by codes and standards. In other cases, due to practical difficulties or unusual circumstances that would adversely affect the building design or operation without compromising safety, a performance-based design will assist in establishing that the intended level of safety of the applicable code or regulation is met. This guide serves as a resource for developing equivalent means of protection to prescriptive requirements.

1.4.6   Performance-based designs executed through the equivalency option are typically applied for a specific feature of the building or associated fire safety system rather than for the entire building design. This is in contrast to the application of the regulation's performance-based design option, in which the entire building or large portions of the building would be designed in accordance to the performance-based design provisions.

1.4.7   Examples of performance-based design can be found in the case study volumes from the biannual SFPE International Conferences on Performance-Based Codes and Fire Safety Design Methods[1, 2, 3] and in Supplement 7 of the NFPA *Life Safety Code® Handbook*.[4]

1.5 Technical References and Resources

1.5.1 Selection of Technical Information   An important part of a performance-based design is the selection and application of engineering standards, calculation methods, and other forms of scientific information that are appropriate for the particular application and methodology used. The engineer and other technically qualified stakeholders should determine the acceptability of the sources and methodologies for the particular applications in which they are to be used. The acceptability of the sources and methodologies selected for particular applications should be subjected to qualified technical review.

1.5.2 Acceptance of References The sources, methodologies, and data used in performance-based designs should be based on technical references that are widely accepted and utilized by the appropriate professions and professional groups. Acceptance of references is often based on documents that are developed, reviewed, and validated under one the following processes:

1. Codes developed under an open consensus process conducted by recognized professional societies, code-making organizations, or governmental bodies

2. Technical references that are subject to a peer review process and are published in widely recognized peer-reviewed journals, conference reports, or other publications

3. Resource publications such as *The SFPE Handbook of Fire Protection Engineering*,[5] which are widely recognized technical sources of information

1.5.3 Acceptability Factors The following factors are helpful in determining the acceptability of the individual method or source:

1. Extent of general acceptance in the relevant professional community. Indications of this acceptance include peer-reviewed publication, widespread citation in the technical literature, and adoption by or within a consensus document.

2. Extent of documentation of the method, including the analytical method itself, assumptions, scope, limitations, data sources, and data reduction methods.

3. Extent of validation and analysis of uncertainties. This includes comparison of the overall method with experimental data to estimate error rates as well as analysis of the uncertainties of input data, uncertainties and limitations in the analytical method, and uncertainties in the associated performance criteria.

4. Extent to which the method is based on sound scientific principles.

5. Extent to which the proposed application is within the stated scope and limitations of the supporting information, including the range of applicability for which there is documented validation. Factors such as spatial

dimensions, occupant characteristics, and ambient conditions might limit valid applications.

6. Extent to which the method has been subjected to qualified technical review.

1.5.4 Component Analyses   In many cases, a method will be built from and include numerous component analyses. These component analyses should be evaluated using the same factors as are applied to the overall method as outlined in 1.5.3.

1.5.5 Limitations   A method to address a specific fire safety issue, within documented limitations or validation regimes, might not exist. In such a case, sources and calculation methods can be used outside of their limitations provided the engineer recognizes the limitations and addresses the resulting implications.

1.5.6 Evaluation of References and Methodologies   The technical references and methodologies to be used in a performance-based design should be closely evaluated by the engineer and technically qualified stakeholders and by a third party reviewer. The strength of the technical justification should be judged using criteria listed in section 1.5.3. This justification might be strengthened by the presence of data obtained from fire testing.

1.5.7 Acceptability Determination   As a convenience to the user, this guide refers to selected technical references and resources that are known to be used by the fire protection community at the time of publication. This is not an all-inclusive list of documents, nor is it an endorsement of specific sources or methodologies that might be contained within the documents. It is still the responsibility of the engineer and stakeholders to determine the acceptability of using any of these technical reference sources or methodologies in a particular performance-based design.

1.6 Review of Performance-Based Designs

1.6.1   All performance-based designs should be subject to the publication of their technical bases and to effective peer review.

1.6.2   The effective peer review of performance-based designs should follow a well-defined and documented process, such as the process described in the document entitled "Guidelines for Peer Review in the Fire Protection

Design Process" published by the Society of Fire Protection Engineers (included in this guide as Appendix H.).

Notes

1. Case Studies, 3rd International Conference on Performance-Based Codes and Fire Safety Design Methods, Society of Fire Protection Engineers, Bethesda, MD, 2000.

2. Case Studies, 4th International Conference on Performance-Based Codes and Fire Safety Design Methods, Society of Fire Protection Engineers, Bethesda, MD, 2002.

3. Case Studies, 5th International Conference on Performance-Based Codes and Fire Safety Design Methods, Society of Fire Protection Engineers, Bethesda, MD, 2004.

4. Puchovsky, M. & Quiter, J. "Supplement 7—The Application of Performance-Based Design Concepts for Fire and Life Safety," *Life Safety Code® Handbook*, National Fire Protection Association, Quincy, MA, 2006.

5. Dinenno, P., ed. *The SFPE Handbook of Fire Protection Engineering*, 3rd Edition, National Fire Protection Association, Quincy, MA, 2002.

CHAPTER 2

Glossary

This chapter defines terms as they will be used in this book. Note that explanatory text is in italics and is enclosed in parentheses.

Alternative Design Solution See "performance-based design option."

Authority Having Jurisdiction (AHJ) An organization, office, or individual responsible for approving designs, equipment, installations, materials, and/or procedures. (*Also, see the definition of "Code Official."*)

Building Any structure used or intended for supporting or sheltering any use or occupancy.

Building Characteristics A set of data that provides a detailed description of a building, such as building layout (geometry), access and egress, construction, building materials, contents, building services, and fire safety (hardware) systems (*see Section 8.2.3.3*).

Client The party for which professional services are rendered.

Code Official[1] The code enforcement officer or other designated authority charged by the applicable governing body with the duties of administration and enforcement of a code, including duly authorized representatives. (*Also, see the definition of "Authority Having Jurisdiction."*)

Confidence Interval A statistical range with a specified probability that a given parameter lies within the range.

Design Criteria See "Performance Criteria."

Design Fire Curve An engineering description of the development of a fire for use in a design fire scenario. (*Design fire curves could be described in terms of heat release rate vs. time or in other terms [see Section 8.5.4]*).

Design Fire Scenario A fire scenario used for the analysis of a design (*see Section 8.5*).

Design Objective A description of the performance benchmark against which the predicted performance of a design is evaluated.

Deterministic Analysis A methodology based on physical relationships derived from scientific theories and empirical results that for a given set of initial conditions will always produce the same result or prediction.

Final Design The design selected for implementation from the successful trial designs.

Fire Characteristics A set of data that provides a description of a fire (*see Section 8.2.3.5*).

Fire Model Physical or mathematical model used to simulate or predict fire characteristics and conditions of the fire environment.

Fire Protection Engineering Design Brief A document summarizing the agreed upon performance criteria and methods that will be used to evaluate trial designs (*see Chapter 11*).

Fire Safety Goals Desired overall fire safety outcome expressed in qualitative terms.

Fire Scenario A set of conditions that defines the development of fire and the spread of combustion products throughout a building or portion of a building, the reactions of people to fire, and the effects of combustion products (*see Section 8.2*).

Frequency The number of times an event is likely to occur within a specified time interval.

Hazard A possible source of danger that can initiate or cause undesirable consequences if uncontrolled.

Objective Requirement of the fire, building, system, or occupants that needs to be fulfilled in order to achieve a fire safety goal. (*Objectives are stated in more specific terms than goals. In general, objectives define a series of actions necessary to make the achievement of a goal more likely.*)

Occupant Characteristics A set of data that describes conditions, abilities, or behaviors of people before and during a fire (*see Section 8.2.3.4*).

Performance-Based Code A code or standard that specifically states its fire safety goals and references acceptable methods that can be used to demonstrate compliance with its requirements.

Performance-Based Design An engineering approach to fire protection design based on: (1) agreed on fire safety goals and objectives; (2) deterministic and/or probabilistic analysis of fire scenarios; and (3) quantitative assessment of design alternatives against the fire safety goals and objectives using accepted engineering tools, methodologies, and performance criteria.

Performance-Based Design Option An option within a code whereby compliance is achieved by demonstrating that a proposed design will meet specified fire safety goals using an engineering analysis. (*More specifically, fire safety goals and objectives are translated into performance* *objectives and performance criteria. Fire models and calculations and other verification methods are used in combination with the building design specifications, specified fire scenarios, and specified assumptions to determine whether the performance criteria are met, in which case there is compliance with the Code under the performance-based design option.*)

Performance Criteria Criteria that are stated in engineering terms, against which the adequacy of any developed trial designs will be judged.

Prescriptive-Based Code A code or standard that prescribes fire safety for a generic use or application. Fire safety is achieved by specifying certain construction characteristics, limiting dimensions, or protection systems without referring to how these requirements achieve a desired fire safety goal.

Prescriptive-Based Design Option An option within a code whereby compliance is achieved by demonstrating adherence to specified construction characteristics, limits on dimensions, protection systems, or other features.

Probabilistic Analysis An assessment of fire losses and fire consequences that includes consideration of the likelihood of different fire scenarios and the inputs that define those fire scenarios.

Probability The likelihood that a given event will occur. (*Probabilities are inherently unitless and expressed as a number between zero and one, inclusive. Where relevant statistical data is available, the probability of an event may be inferred from the ratio of the number of actual occurrences of the event to the total number of possible occurrences.*)

Project Scope An identification of the range or extent of the design matter being addressed, including any specific limits of a performance-based design. (*This identification could be a subset of a larger development, evaluation, or design effort [e.g., one part of the building design process] or a stand-alone fire safety analysis and design project*).

Risk In the classical engineering sense, risk is the product of the potential consequences and the expected frequency of occurrence. (*Consequences could include occupant death, monetary loss, business interruption, environmental damage, etc. The frequency of occurrence could be an estimate of how often the projected loss could occur.*)

Safety Factor Adjustment made to compensate for uncertainty in the methods, calculations, and assumptions employed in developing engineering designs.

Stakeholder One who has a share or an interest, as in an enterprise. (*Specifically, an individual, or representative of same, having an interest in the successful completion of a project that could be financial, safety related, etc. Not all stakeholders have equal authority or input into the process. The degree of stakeholder involvement depends on many factors, including the type of project management and delivery system [see Section 4.2.4]*).

Stakeholder Objective A statement of a stakeholder's level of acceptable or sustainable loss.

Trial Design A fire protection system design intended to achieve the stated fire safety goals and expressed in terms that make it possible to assess whether the fire safety goals have been achieved.

Uncertainty The amount by which an observed or calculated value could differ from the true value. Deviations between reality and the model predictions due to limits in scientific knowledge, simplified assumptions, and approximations in calculations (*see Section 10.5*).

Verification Confirmation that a proposed solution meets the established fire safety goals. (*Verification of a performance-based design could involve alternate computer fire models to reproduce results, conducting large/full scale fire testing, etc.*)

Worst Case Scenario Scenario resulting in the worst maximum consequence as defined by the stakeholders or a code. Criteria must be explicitly stated, since "worst case" conditions for life safety and property protection could be incompatible. (*Also, see the definition of "Worst Credible Fire."*)

Worst Credible Fire For a specific site, a fire as defined by the stakeholders or a code that can be reasonably expected to result in unfavorable consequences equal to or less severe than those resulting from a worst case scenario.

Note

1. *SFPE Code Official's Guide to Performance-Based Design Review*, International Code Council, Falls Church, VA, 2004.

CHAPTER 3

Overview of the Performance-Based Fire Protection Analysis and Design Process

3.1 General

3.1.1 This guide can be used for the development and evaluation of designs of fire protection measures to achieve stated fire and life safety objectives, to support the development of alternatives to prescriptive-based code requirements, or to evaluate the building fire safety design as a whole.

3.1.2 The process in this guide is applicable to the analysis of new and existing buildings. Performance-based fire protection analysis and design is one element in the overall process of building design, construction, and operation.

3.1.3 The performance-based design (PBD) process most appropriately begins during the feasibility or conceptual design phase when key decisions are being made (see Section 1.1.1). The earlier the engineer becomes involved in the building design and construction process, the greater the benefits realized. These benefits include the following:

- Design flexibility
- Innovation in design, construction, and materials
- Equal or better fire safety
- Maximization of the benefit/cost ratio

A representative basic building design and construction process is outlined in Figure 3-1. The boxes containing the terms Feasibility Study and

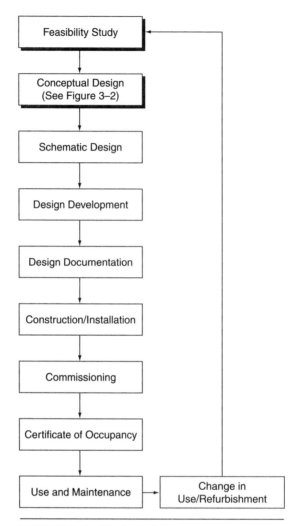

FIGURE 3-1 Basic Building Design and Construction Process

Conceptual Design are shadowed in the figure to indicate the importance of involving the engineer early in the overall design process. See Section 3.1.7 for more information.

3.1.4 The team approach is essential to the success of a performance-based design. The team often consists of the owner(s), designers, and the authorities having jurisdiction (AHJs) and other stakeholders, as identified in Chapter 4. The responsibility and authority of each stakeholder should be identified.

Together, they should set a framework that fosters good communications and a clear understanding of the goals and objectives of the performance-based design. A basic agreement should be reached in the initial stages on the fundamental aspects of any specific performance-based design. The basic agreement encompasses the setting of goals and objectives. A schedule for meetings, reviews, deliverables, and the permitting and inspection process and associated fees are also important.

3.1.5   During the design development and construction documentation phases, the conceptual designs evolve into detailed designs of systems and the plans and specifications that will be used for bidding and constructing the building. The design development and construction documentation phases are not described in this guide. However, guidance for the coordination of design documentation is provided in Chapter 12. Coordination between disciplines is critical during these phases in order to ensure proper interaction between systems.

3.1.6   The concepts utilized in the performance-based design process, including the limitations and assumptions, must be reviewed by the stakeholders throughout the design process. Design changes resulting from value engineering or other design procedures must be incorporated in the performance-based design analysis. For example, changes to systems seemingly unrelated to fire safety, such as the bathroom exhaust systems or operable windows, could affect a performance-based design incorporating smoke control systems.

3.1.7   Commissioning of fire protection systems and features and review of their installation to validate that they meet the proposed intent of the design is essential to the level of fire safety provided in the structure. The engineer should be involved in the production and review of design documents, review of shop drawings, field inspections, and acceptance testing of the fire protection systems.

3.1.8   After the building is commissioned and the certificate of occupancy is issued, the building owner should assure that the building is used and maintained in accordance with the fire protection concepts incorporated in the original performance-based design. The assurance from the building owner can be accomplished by implementation of operation and maintenance criteria specified in the operations and maintenance manuals for the building that should be developed by the engineer. (See Chapter 12.) The stakeholders must recognize that a performance-based design could impose constraints on the future of the building. If a change of use or occupancy is inconsistent with the original design assumptions and conditions, the design process as illustrated in Figure 3-1 should be repeated for the change in use/refurbishment.

Because of the unique assumptions and fire protection concepts that could be incorporated in a performance-based design, the development and maintenance of accurate documentation is critical. The building owner, authority having jurisdiction, engineers, and other stakeholders involved in the operation, use, and modification of a building could change during the life of a building. Complete, accurate documentation provides a means for future stakeholders to understand and function within the limitations of the original design assumptions and conditions.

3.2 Team Approach and Roles of the Team Members

3.2.1 Team Qualifications
As previously noted, a team approach is essential to the success of a performance-based design project. It is also essential that both the owner's representatives and the AHJ's representatives have sufficient knowledge in the area(s) of fire protection engineering that are related to the needs of the performance-based design project. Determination of whether an individual is qualified can be accomplished by reviewing his or her education, licenses, and certifications, and a record of his or her experience.

3.2.2 Owner's Role
The owner is responsible for the selection and compensation of qualified design professionals and special experts with sufficient knowledge in the areas relevant to the performance-based design. Often, a principal design professional is required to coordinate the efforts of multiple designers. If the owner cannot attend meetings and carry out his or her responsibilities, then a designated representative who is empowered to act on behalf of the owner at meetings and all stages of the process is necessary for the success of the project. The owner must agree to project assumptions, limitations, and risks.

3.2.3 Principal Design Professional's Role
The principal design professional has overall responsibility for a complete and comprehensive design and is responsible for the coordination of designers and special experts. This responsibility should include, but is not limited to, the preparation of reports, investigations, and a comprehensive set of construction documents. Coordination among the designers and special experts and the owner is also needed for the reviews and submittals, as well as the submittals and the reviews by the AHJ and/or peer reviewer. The principal design professional

might perform some or all of the design tasks associated with a project, or might delegate these tasks to other design professionals or special experts. Federal, state, or local law could require that the principal design professional be registered or licensed in the state or jurisdiction in which the construction will be undertaken.

3.2.4 Fire Protection Design Professional's Role
Fire protection design professionals are often directed by the principal design professional to perform specific tasks. Fire protection design professionals should have an understanding of or an ability to interpret the level of safety intended by the codes or standards relevant to the project and the ability to demonstrate and document the achievement of acceptable levels of protection. Fire protection design professionals should have sufficient relevant knowledge to know which approaches could be used to perform the tasks and the applicability and limitations of the method(s) that they select. Examples of areas that fire protection design professionals often need to understand include the following:

- Fire dynamics
- Fire modeling
- Active and passive fire protection systems
- Fire testing
- Fire department operations
- Human behavior

Federal, state, or local law could require that fire protection design professionals be registered or licensed in the state or jurisdiction in which the construction will be undertaken; however, licensing requirements could depend upon the scope or roles of the professionals in the project.

3.2.5 Special Expert's Role
Special experts could be used by design professionals to perform specific tasks within their area of expertise. It may not be necessary to have professional licensing in order for special experts to be qualified. The qualifications of special experts can be determined through a review of their education and experience.

3.2.6 Construction Personnel's Role
The construction manager, general contractor, or subcontractors might have to coordinate and commission complex design aspects that are not present in a design that was prepared to meet prescriptive requirements. It is imperative that construction

personnel understand that they must comply with the documentation of the performance-based design and implement any special requirements or installation methods that result from the design. Construction personnel normally are not licensed to adequately serve in this capacity. Their close coordination with the licensed design professionals and the AHJs is critical for the successful construction of the performance-based design (PBD) project.

3.2.7 Facility Staff's Role

Facility staff should be able to represent the owner's interest as it affects the design, inspection, testing, and maintenance requirements of the performance-based designed systems. Facility staff should become familiar with necessary record keeping and bounding conditions of the specific performance-based design for their project. A representative of the facility staff should know to check the operations and maintenance manual to be aware of when proposed renovations could impact the original design. Additionally, facility staff should have the authority to perform actions needed to ensure continued compliance.

3.2.8 AHJ's Role

The AHJ is responsible for acquiring competent reviewers/inspectors and for utilizing registered, licensed, or certified individuals when required by a state or jurisdiction. The AHJ should have the responsibility of ensuring that the goals and objectives of the adopted codes and ordinances of the jurisdiction are identified and addressed. If the required expertise is not contained within the current staff, its acquisition must be addressed (i.e., via contract review or peer review). If peer review will be used to ensure the proper expertise, this should be identified early in the design process. The AHJ must be committed to following through with agreed-on decisions and assumptions for the project. The AHJ's responsibilities will include the scheduling, approval, permitting process, and the commitment of staffing. The AHJ should provide acceptance or rejection of the approach upon its completion. If the design complies with the performance requirements, approval should be granted. If not, the design should be rejected, with a written explanation of the reasons for rejection. The AHJ should ensure that a mechanism is in place to retain the documentation relevant to design-bounding conditions, construction, and inspection.

3.2.9 Peer Reviewer's Role

The peer reviewer is responsible for reviewing the performance-based design either partially or in its entirety, to assure conformance to the stated goals, objectives, or other conditions as outlined in the design. The Peer Review Guidelines prepared by the Society of Fire Protection Engineers provides further information on the role of peer reviewers in the process. These guidelines are found in Appendix H of this guide.

3.3 Performance-Based Design Process

3.3.1 Steps Recommended
In the performance-based design process, there can be many acceptable approaches that will efficiently address and resolve a performance-based design issue. For example, the stakeholders can rank trial designs based on financial consideration, desired building features, and other factors. The engineer could then evaluate the highest ranked trial design against the design fire scenarios to determine if the trial design meets the performance criteria. In outlining a process, this guide does not intend to mandate one process over other alternatives, but does identify the following process steps that should guide a performance-based design in a complete and comprehensive manner. The recommended steps in the performance-based design process are discussed in Sections 3.3.2 through 3.3.11 and Chapters 4 through 13. The flowchart shown in Figure 3-2 is used in Chapter 4 through Chapter 12 with the subject of each chapter highlighted in the flowchart as appropriate. The purpose of the flowchart is to provide the user with an idea of where each chapter fits in the overall performance-based design process.

3.3.2 Define Project Scope
The first step in a performance-based design is to define the scope of the project. See Chapter 4. Defining the scope consists of identifying and documenting the following:

- Constraints on the design and project schedule
- The stakeholders associated with the project
- The proposed building construction and features desired by the owner or tenant
- Occupant characteristics and building characteristics
- The intended use and occupancy of the building
- Applicable codes and regulations
- The project management and delivery method (e.g., design-build), which can define the extent of involvement of the fire protection engineer conducting the performance-based analysis

An understanding of these items is needed to ensure that a performance-based design meets the stakeholders' needs.

3.3.3 Identify Goals
Once the scope of the project is defined, the next step in the performance-based design process is to identify and document the fire safety goals of various stakeholders. See Chapter 5 for details. Among others, fire safety goals could include levels of protection for people and

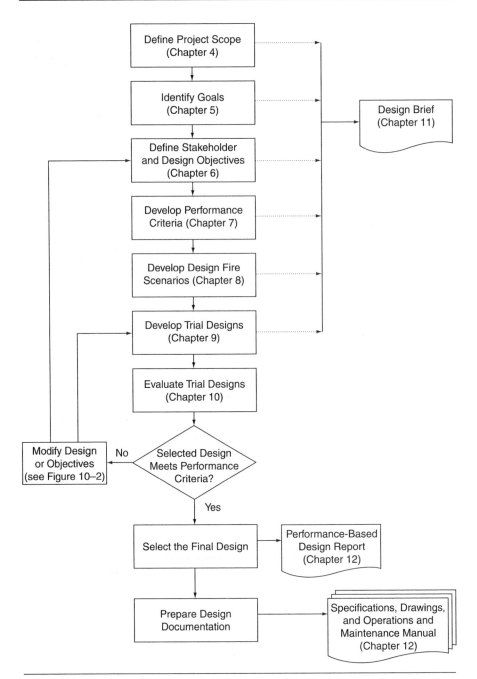

FIGURE 3-2   Steps in the Performance-Based Analysis and the Conceptual Design Procedure for Fire Protection Design

property or provide for continuity of operations, historical preservation, and environmental protection. Goals could be unique for different projects, based on the stakeholders' needs and desires.

The stakeholders should discuss which goals are the most important for the project. To avoid problems later in the design process, all stakeholders should be aware of and agree to the goals before proceeding with the performance-based design process.

3.3.4 Define Objectives

The third step in the design process is to develop objectives. See Chapter 6. The objectives are essentially the design goals that are further refined into tangible values that can be quantified in engineering terms. Objectives could include mitigating the consequences of a fire expressed in terms of dollar values, loss of life, or other impacts on property operations, or maximum allowable conditions, such as the extent of fire spread, temperature, and spread of combustion products.

3.3.5 Develop Performance Criteria

The fourth step in the design process is to develop performance criteria to be met by the design. These criteria are a further refinement of the design objectives and are numerical values to which the expected performance of the trial designs can be compared. See Chapter 7. Among other values, performance criteria could include threshold values for temperatures of materials, gas temperatures, carboxyhemoglobin (COHb) levels, smoke obscuration, and thermal exposure levels.

3.3.6 Develop Fire Scenarios and Design Fire Scenarios

Once the performance criteria have been established, the engineer develops and analyzes design alternatives to meet performance criteria. The first part of this process is to identify possible fire scenarios and design fire scenarios. See Chapter 8.

Fire scenarios are descriptions of possible fire events and consist of fire characteristics, building characteristics, and occupant characteristics. The fire scenarios identified are subsequently filtered (i.e., combined or eliminated) into a subset of design fire scenarios against which trial designs are evaluated.

3.3.7 Develop Trial Design(s)

Once the project scope, performance criteria, and design fire scenarios are established, the designer develops preliminary design(s), which are intended to meet the project requirements. These are referred to as trial designs. See Chapter 9.

The trial design(s) include proposed fire protection systems, construction features and operations that are provided in order for a design to meet the performance criteria when evaluated using the design fire scenarios.

The method of evaluation should also be determined at this point. The methods used to perform the evaluation must be appropriate for the application in which they are used and be agreeable to the stakeholders.

3.3.8 Prepare Fire Protection Engineering Design Brief   A fire protection engineering design brief should be prepared and provided to all stakeholders for their review and concurrence. (See Chapter 11). The brief can be started concurrently with any prior step in the process and finalized at this point in time. This brief should document the project scope, goals, objectives, trial design(s), performance criteria, design fire scenarios, and analysis methods. Documenting and agreeing upon these factors helps avoid possible misunderstandings at a later date.

3.3.9 Evaluate Trial Design(s)   Each trial design is then evaluated using each design fire scenario. See Chapter 10. The results of each evaluation indicate whether the trial design meets the performance criteria.

Only trial design(s) that meet the performance criteria can be considered as a final design proposal. If the stakeholders agree, the design or objectives may be revised. The criteria cannot be arbitrarily changed to ensure that a trial design meets the criterion, but can be changed based on additional analysis and/or consideration of additional data.

3.3.10 Select the Final Design   Once an acceptable trial design is identified by the evaluation, it can be considered for the final project design. If multiple trial designs are evaluated, further analysis is needed to select a final design. The choice of which acceptable trial design is selected for the final design could be based on a variety of different factors, including financial considerations, timeliness of installation, system and material availability, ease of installation, maintenance and use, and other factors.

3.3.11 Design Documentation   Once the final design is identified, design documents need to be prepared. See Chapter 12. Proper documentation ensures that all stakeholders understand what is necessary for the design implementation, maintenance, and continuity of the fire protection design.

The documentation should include the fire protection engineering design brief, a performance design report, detailed specifications and drawings, and a building operations and maintenance manual.

3.3.12 Manage Changes   The continued success of a performance-based design requires adherence to the design criteria throughout the life cycle of the facility. (See Chapter 13). This life cycle may involve changes in individual stakeholders, including owners, facility tenants, management,

and maintenance staff, as well as changes in desired facility configurations and occupancy. It is critical that these changes be managed through recognition and adherence to facility maintenance manuals and established procedures for the approval and documentation of facility usage and configuration alterations.

3.4 Application and Use

3.4.1 Application
The performance-based design process described in this guide can be used in conjunction with prescriptive-based codes, with performance-based codes, or as a stand-alone engineering analysis and design effort.

3.4.2 Use With Prescriptive-Based Codes

3.4.2.1 Prescriptive-based codes provide requirements for broad classifications of buildings. These requirements are generally stated in terms of fixed values, such as maximum travel distance, minimum fire resistance ratings, and minimum features of required systems (e.g., detection, alarm, suppression, and ventilation).

In most prescriptive-based codes, however, there is an "alternative methods and materials" or "equivalency" clause that permits, at the discretion of the authority having jurisdiction (AHJ), the use of alternative means to meet the intent of the prescribed code provisions. This clause provides an opportunity for using a performance-based design approach via a standardized methodology. Through performance-based design, it can be demonstrated whether a building design is satisfactory and complies with the implicit or explicit intent of the applicable code.

3.4.2.2 When employing the alternative materials and methods or equivalency clause, it is important to identify the prescriptive-based code provision being addressed (scope) to provide the following: an interpretation of the intent of the provision (goals and objectives), an alternative approach (trial design), and engineering support for the suggested alternative (evaluate trial designs). This guide provides a framework for addressing these issues in a logical and consistent manner.

3.4.2.3 Trial designs require a comparison of the performance of the design features required by a prescriptive-based code with the performance resulting from the trial design. Using prescribed features as a baseline for comparison (i.e., as the performance criteria), it can be demonstrated in the evaluation whether or not a trial design offers the intended level of performance.

A comparison of safety provided can provide the basis for establishing equivalency of performance-based designs.

3.4.2.4   When a trial design does not meet or exceed the level of performance prescribed by code, failure of the trial design could be assumed. Further review of the evaluation could reveal excesses in the prescribed code fire protection approach. These excesses could exist when the performance of a prescribed code design provides a sufficiently large margin of safety beyond that required by the performance criteria.

3.4.3 Use with Performance-Based Codes

3.4.3.1   Performance-based codes establish acceptable or tolerable levels of hazard or risk for a variety of health, safety, and public welfare issues in buildings. Unlike prescriptive-based codes, however, the levels of acceptable or tolerable risk are often expressed qualitatively, in phrases such as "safeguard people from injury due to fire" and "give people adequate time to reach a safe place," rather than in terms of specific construction requirements.

3.4.3.2   In performance-based codes, the code writers essentially qualify (and sometimes quantify) the level of risk acceptable to society (the "stakeholders" or users of the code). As this is much more difficult to agree on than the acceptable level of risk for an individual stakeholder, several countries handle this issue by stating fire safety goals as broad social objectives, such as "safeguard people from injury due to fire," and providing more detailed performance objectives or functional objectives, such as "give people adequate time to reach a safe place."

3.4.3.3   The use of terms such as "adequate" and "reasonable" permit design flexibility and provide general guidance on the level of risk society or a specific community is willing to accept without stating specifics. It is assumed that if a "reasonable" approach has been taken in determining "an adequate time to reach a safe place," the recommended safety measures will be "acceptable."

3.4.3.4   Compliance with performance-based codes is typically attained by using either a prescriptive-based code that has been "deemed to comply" as an "acceptable solution," or by using a performance-based design approach that provides an "acceptable method" for developing an "acceptable solution,"

3.4.4 Use as a Stand-Alone Methodology

3.4.4.1   In many cases, prescriptive-based codes are the basis of an analysis and design project. However, additional or complementary fire safety goals and objectives could be identified, thus requiring additional fire protection engineering analysis and design.

For example, property protection and continuity of operations could be goals of a building owner or insurer, yet not fully addressed in local building and fire codes. The performance-based design process can be used to identify and address the additional goals.

3.4.4.2　To address such additional or complementary goals, the performance-based design process outlined in this guide provides a structured approach for addressing a variety of fire safety issues while providing design flexibility.

3.5　Levels of Application

3.5.1　The performance-based design process can be used to evaluate and recommend fire protection options at the subsystem performance level, at the system performance level, or at the building performance level. At any level, the results could be evaluated on a comparative or absolute basis.

3.5.2　A subsystem performance evaluation typically consists of a simple comparative analysis in which it is required to demonstrate that a selected subsystem provides "equivalent" performance to that specified by a prescriptive-based code. At this level, one subsystem is evaluated in isolation.

3.5.3　A system performance evaluation could consist of a comparative or absolute analysis. A system performance evaluation is used when more than one fire protection system or feature is involved. A system performance evaluation is more complex than a subsystem evaluation, as the analysis needs to take account of the interaction between various subsystems.

3.5.4　In a building performance analysis, all subsystems used in the protection strategy and their interactions are considered. A performance-based design that takes into account total building fire safety can provide more comprehensive solutions than subsystem or system performance analyses, because the entire building-fire-target interaction is evaluated.

3.5.5　See Section 10.2 for additional information on the levels of analysis.

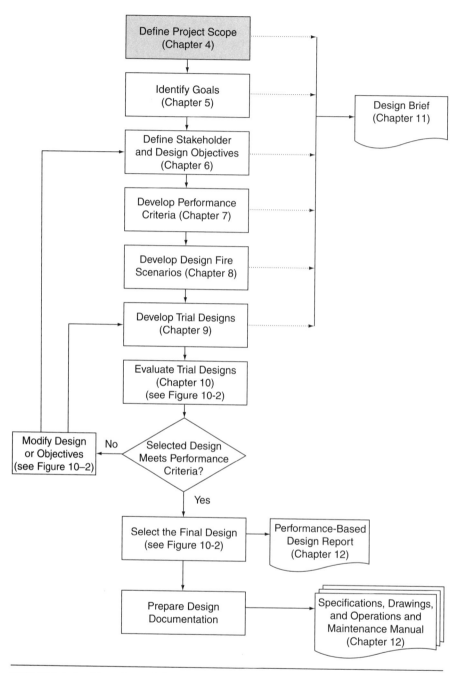

FIGURE 4-1 Overview of the Performance-Based Design Process, Defining Project Scope

CHAPTER 4

Defining Project Scope

4.1 General

The first step in the process of conducting a performance-based analysis or design is to determine the scope of the project. Figure 4-1 illustrates how this step fits into the overall process.

4.2 Project Scope

4.2.1 Definition   The project scope is an identification of the boundaries of the performance-based analysis or design. The boundaries of the design could include: building use, design intent, project constraints, design and construction team organization (traditional versus design build), project schedules, and applicable regulations.

4.2.2 Contents   The scope can include the following:

- Specific fire protection system components, a partial building, a whole building, or several buildings
- New construction or renovation of an existing building, either for a change in use or modernization
- Repairs to a partial building, a whole building, or several buildings

4.2.3 Budget   In addition to physical limitations on the scope, budgetary parameters can affect the cost-benefit of a performance-based design. Therefore, the available budget for the analysis and for possible solutions should also be determined.

4.2.4 Stakeholders
The scope of the project can vary depending on the perspective of the design participant. Therefore, all stakeholders in the project should be identified. The stakeholders should establish goals and objectives. Example stakeholders are as follows:

- Building owner
- Building manager
- Design team
- Authorities having jurisdiction (AHJs)
    - Fire
    - Building
    - Insurance
- Accreditation agencies
- Construction team
    - Construction manager
    - General contractor
    - Subcontractors
- Tenants
- Building operations and maintenance
- Emergency responders
- Peer reviewer

4.2.4.1 Each stakeholder identified could have similar, different, or additional goals and objectives. It is imperative for the engineer to identify the stakeholders in order to obtain acceptance of the performance-based strategies used in the process. Concurrence from the stakeholders at the beginning improves chances of acceptance of the performance-based design alternatives. This is particularly important with regard to the authorities having jurisdiction. The earlier in the process that AHJs get involved, the better. Early involvement can provide opportunities for the AHJ's concerns to be addressed before significant effort is put into the project. In some cases, the AHJ may not have staff with appropriate expertise to review and address a performance-based design. If no one in the current staff has the required expertise, its acquisition must be addressed (i.e., via contract review or peer review). If peer review will be part of the process to ensure that the proper expertise exists, the need for this review should be identified early in the design process. If the AHJs or the assigned peer reviewer are not involved until the final submittal, the amount of additional effort required to address concerns can be substantial.

4.2.4.2   It is important to recognize that stakeholders have varying levels of responsibility and authority over different aspects of the project. Some will have approval authority while others may act in a review or advisory capacity. It can be important to identify the role and responsibility of each stakeholder depending upon the project management and delivery system as well as jurisdictional requirements.

4.3 Submittal Schedule

4.3.1 Format   A submittal schedule should be established as part of the project scope either as a stand-alone document or as part of another project document.

4.3.2 Approvals   The submittal schedule should list each project deliverable and who must approve the document. Approvals by multiple stakeholders could be required; however, it is not necessary or expected that each stakeholder will approve each document.

4.3.3 Order of Approvals   For some projects, the approval order for each respective stakeholder can be a concern. If this is the case, this information should be part of the submittal schedule.

4.3.4 Distribution of Copies   It is also appropriate for the submittal schedule to specify who should get a copy of the project documentation, intermediate deliverables, and when they are expected.

4.4 Project Scope Issues

4.4.1 Building and Occupant Characteristics   The engineer must understand a building's proposed use and the characteristics of the occupants when undertaking a performance-based analysis or design. The building's functional, geometric, and operational characteristics will be the basis for developing fire scenarios.

4.4.2 Other Issues   In addition to building characteristics and occupant characteristics, other types of issues that could affect design performance should be considered. The following list is intended to be representative and should not be considered to be all-inclusive.

4.4.2.1 *Property Location* The location of the property, site conditions, and the locations of adjacent properties should be determined.

4.4.2.2 *Fire Service Characteristics* The location, expected response time, operating procedures, and capabilities of the fire service and applicable emergency responders should be determined.

4.4.2.3 *Utilities* The location and capacity of site utilities such as drainage, fuel, water, and electric supply should be determined.

4.4.2.4 *Environmental Considerations* Land use planning, effluent production, wetlands, zoning classifications, and pollution considerations should be considered.

4.4.2.5 *Historic Preservation (if applicable)* Preservation could be an issue if it affects subsequent objectives and design options.

4.4.2.6 *Building Management and Security* The planned management and security schemes for the building should be ascertained.

4.4.2.7 *Economic and Social Value of the Building* Economic value could include tax base or employment considerations. Social value could include historic, public assembly, or religious significance.

4.4.2.8 *Project Delivery Process* There are several forms of project organization and delivery. Traditional architect/engineering lead projects, design-build, fast track, and a host of other delivery methods will affect the development, implementation, and evaluation of the performance-based design.

4.4.2.8.1 The project management and delivery system can influence the performance-based fire protection analysis and design process. With the advent of several project management and delivery methods, the role of the fire protection engineer and the stakeholders may vary significantly. For example, the traditional "design-bid-build" process tends to place more control of the performance-based design in the hands of the design team. On the other hand, a "design-build" process may relegate the responsibility of the fire protection engineer to the development of the conceptual fire protection design. It is important that the stakeholders understand the contractual obligation and scope of services to be provided by the engineer performing the performance-based design.

4.4.2.8.2   The American Institute of Architects and the Associated General Contractors of America publish a document, *"Primer on Private Delivery,"*[1] which addresses in detail the various methods of project delivery.

4.4.2.9 Applicable Regulations   The engineer should identify the appropriate codes, regulations, and insurance requirements for the performance-based analysis.

4.4.2.10 Documentation of Assumptions   When an issue is not known, a reasonable assumption may be made. However, the stakeholders might need to take steps to ensure that the assumption is valid during the life of the building. Any assumptions must be documented as described in Chapter 12.

4.4.2.11 Identification of Roles   The role, responsibility, and approval authority will vary among the stakeholders and various team members depending upon the project management and delivery process and applicable jurisdictional requirements. Roles should be clearly identified at the very beginning of the process and agreed upon by the client, the authority having jurisdiction, and any other stakeholder who can approve the performance-based design.

4.4.3 Predetermined Issues   The issues identified in Sections 4.4.2 through 4.4.2.11 may have been predetermined in advance of the performance-based design. However, even predetermined issues can sometimes change as part of the performance-based design. The engineer should consult with other stakeholders to determine the ability to change items identified as a part of the scope of the project.

Note

1. "Primer on Project Delivery," The American Institute of Architects and The Associated General Contractors of America, Washington, DC, 2004.

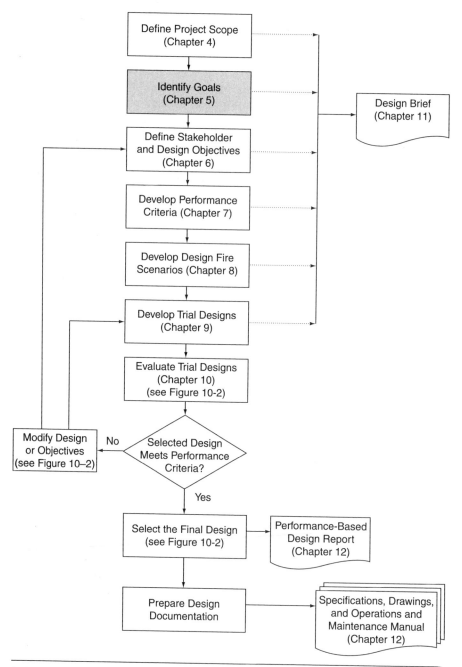

FIGURE 5-1 Overview of the Performance-Based Design Process, Identifying Goals

CHAPTER 5

Identifying Goals

5.1 General

5.1.1   After the project scope has been established, the next step in the performance-based analysis and design process is to identify the fire safety goal(s) of interest to stakeholders (see Figure 5-1) and prioritize those goals for the specific project being addressed.

5.1.2   Goals may come from two possible sources: applicable codes or project stakeholders.

5.1.2.1   Some codes provide the goals that compliance with the code is intended to achieve. For example, *NFPA 5000®*, *Building Construction and Safety Code®,*[7] provides goals related to safety, health, and public welfare. Similarly, the *International Code Council Performance Code*[2] provides goals (that are called "objectives" in the code) relating to a number of hazards. Other codes identify performance goals for specific applications, such as NFPA 914, *Code for Fire Protection of Historic Structures*,[3] and NFPA 130, *Standard for Fixed Guideway Transit and Passenger Rail Systems*.[4] Goals from applicable codes generally need to be met by the design.

5.1.2.2   Whether or not an applicable code states goals, project stakeholders may provide goals. Identifying these types of goals is done through discussions with the stakeholders and review of background materials. Background materials may include occupancy and occupant characteristics, critical elements of business operations, hazard assessments, and general occupancy-specific fire scenarios and loss history.

5.2 Goals for Fire Safety

Fire protection generally has four interrelated fundamental goals for fire safety:

1. *Life safety.* Provide life safety for the public, building occupants, and emergency responders by minimizing fire-related injuries and preventing undue loss of life.

2. *Property protection.* Minimize damage to property and cultural resources from fire (e.g., protect building, contents, and historical features from fire and exposure to and from adjacent buildings).

3. *Continuity of operations.* Provide for continuity of operations (i.e., protect the organization's ongoing mission, production, or operating capability). Minimize undue loss of operations and business-related revenue caused by fire-related damage.

4. *Environmental protection.* Limit the environmental impact of fire from combustion products and release of hazardous materials.

5.3 Related Goals

Securing life, property, operations, and the environment from damage or harm due to fire will often require the implementation of fire protection measures for the control or management of fire. The implementation or operation of such fire protection measures can, however, introduce a potential for non-fire damage that must be considered. Related fire safety goals that might need to be developed and addressed in a performance-based design include, but are not limited to, the following:

1. Provide for historic preservation by identifying a historic building's character-defining spaces, features, and finishes, so that the implementation and the intended or unintended operation of fire protection measures do not result in damage or loss.

2. Provide for protection of the environment by identifying the chemical or biological impact of the installation and the intended or unintended operation of fire protection measures on the natural environment.

5.4 Conflicting Goals

The engineer must understand that there might be competing or conflicting goals. Tenants and architects seek to maximize design flexibility, form, and function while simultaneously seeking a fire-safe environment. For example, architects often want large open interconnected spaces that may pose smoke movement and egress concerns. The authority having jurisdiction may have differing goals based upon statutory requirements, department policy, and applicable codes and standards. Maintenance personnel want fire protection systems that are easy to understand and maintain. Contractors' goals include ease of construction. Each stakeholder could have additional driving issues—time, money, or flexibility. Although the goal-making process should be a collaborative effort, typically the client and the authority having jurisdiction have the final say. The fire protection engineer should consider facilitating or assisting in resolving conflicting goals. If there is a potential impasse, consideration should be given to obtaining outside technical assistance.

5.5 Goal Definition

A fundamental goal is normally defined in broad terms by the stakeholders. There could also be supplemental goals or secondary goals. Table 5-1 contains examples of different types of goals, all of which should be understood by the engineer when conducting a performance-based design.

TABLE 5-1   Examples of Fire Safety Goals

Fundamental Goals

- Minimize fire-related injuries and prevent undue loss of life
- Minimize fire-related damage to the building, its contents, and its historical features and attributes
- Minimize loss of operations and business-related revenue due to fire-related damage
- Limit the environmental impact of the fire and fire protection measures

Other Possible Goals

- Provide sufficient training and awareness to ensure the safety of occupants from fire
- Reduce construction costs while maintaining adequate fire life safety
- Maximize flexibility of operations or building layout after completion
- Minimize damage to historic building fabric from the installation of fire protection features

---

5.6 Methods of Stating Goals

When undertaking a design that is based on a prescriptive-based code, the goal(s) could be embodied in an intent statement. When undertaking a design that is based on a performance-based code, the goal(s) could be embodied in an intent statement, embodied in an objective statement, or clearly stated.

5.7 Setting Priorities

Although it is likely that the stakeholders will share many of the same global goals, the priority and relative weight could vary among stakeholders. Further differences could occur when defining objectives and performance criteria.

5.7.1   Priorities of goals should be based on specifics of the building, its intended use, and the hazards and risks associated with its intended occupancy.

5.7.2   Prioritization helps to clarify the intended use of potential fire protection measures, and helps to identify those aspects of the fire protection analysis and design that may require the most attention. For example, if life safety of the occupants is a high priority, and property protection is a very low priority, the fire protection analysis and design can focus on protecting the people until they reach a place of safety outside the building, and may not have to focus on protecting the building after the people are out of the building. If property protection is also an issue, additional consideration may have to be given to fire fighter safety through analysis of structural response.

5.7.3   It is important to consider that, although the stakeholders might identify only one or two goals as being important, all the goals have to be addressed. (For example, when working with an industrial facility, an engineer could be concerned primarily with process and property protection, yet must also consider life safety issues and environmental issues. Here again, the process of prioritization makes the stakeholders consider a variety of potential concerns.)

Notes

1. *NFPA 5000®, Building Construction and Safety Code®*, 2006 edition, National Fire Protection Association, Quincy, MA.

2. *International Code Council Performance Code*, International Code Council, Falls Church, VA, 2003.

3. NFPA 914, *Code for Fire Protection of Historic Structures*, 2007 edition, National Fire Protection Association, Quincy, MA.

4. NFPA 130, *Standard for Fixed Guideway Transit and Passenger Rail Systems*, 2007 edition, National Fire Protection Association, Quincy, MA.

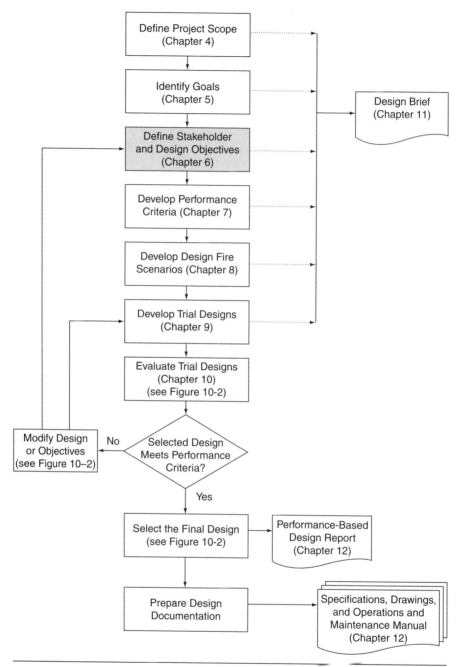

FIGURE 6-1 Overview of the Performance-Based Process, Defining Stakeholder and Design Objectives

CHAPTER 6

Defining Stakeholder Objectives and Design Objectives

6.1 General

6.1.1 Overview Once the fire protection goals have been established and agreed to, stakeholder objectives or the actions needed to meet the fire protection goals must be defined, as shown in Figure 6-1.

6.1.2 Codes That Identify Goals Some codes identify goals. Compliance with the code is intended to meet the intent of such goals.

6.1.2.1 For example, *NFPA 5000®*, *Building Construction and Safety Code®*, provides objectives that further define the goals provided in the code.[1] The *International Code Council Performance Code*[2] also provides objectives (that are called "functional statements" in the code) that follow from the code's goals.

6.1.2.2 If goals were developed in collaboration with project stakeholders, these goals will need to be further defined by the engineer in consultation with the stakeholders.

6.1.3 Stakeholder Objectives A stakeholder objective provides more detail than a fire protection goal, and is often stated in terms of acceptable or sustainable loss or in terms of a desired (acceptable, tolerable) level of risk. By virtue of experience or training, some stakeholders might be able to state objectives in engineering terms, such as critical temperatures for equipment damage that can serve as design objectives or performance criteria.

6.1.3.1   Stakeholder objectives can be based broadly in terms of meeting one or more of the fundamental fire safety goals that are listed in Section 5.2. For example, an objective may be to limit fire injuries beyond the room of fire origin. More specifically, design objectives can be stated in terms of meeting the requirements of a specific code provision (prescriptive- or performance-based), meeting a specific insurance-related requirement, or meeting requirements that go beyond a specific code or insurance requirement. As with goals, objectives that are developed from applicable codes generally need to be met by the design.

6.1.3.2   Specific stakeholder objectives could reflect the following: maximum acceptable (tolerable) extent of injury to persons; damage to a building or its contents; damage to critical equipment or processes in the building; length of downtime or business interruption; risk ranking score; or degree of damage to the environment caused by fire or fire protection measures. Alternatively, stakeholders could express an acceptable loss as either the maximum downtime or the amount of physical damage in dollars. Performance-based codes can specifically provide stakeholder objectives under the classification of Objective, Functional Statement, and/or Performance Objective.

6.1.3.3   The engineer must understand that there can be competing or conflicting objectives. Although the goal-making process should be a collaborative effort, typically the client and the authority having jurisdiction have the final say. The fire protection engineer should consider facilitating or assisting in resolving conflicting design objectives. If there is a potential impasse, consideration should be given to obtaining outside technical assistance.

6.1.3.4   Stakeholder objectives must be clear and agreed to by those involved. The engineer will translate these objectives into numerical engineering values for design purposes.

6.1.3.5   Given that most buildings contain ignition sources, fuels, and oxygen, there is always some possibility that a fire may occur. Similarly, a possibility exists that a fire in an occupied building will result in injury or death, or that a fire in any building will result in property damage or business interruption. Therefore, the engineer must be clear, when communicating with other stakeholders, that an entirely hazard- or risk-free environment cannot be achieved or provided.

6.2 Transforming Stakeholder Objectives into Design Objectives

6.2.1 Quantifiable Terms In order to undertake an engineering analysis and design, stakeholder objectives must first be translated into values that can be quantified in fire protection engineering terms. These terms are the design objectives from which performance criteria can be developed. Quantification can be in deterministic or probabilistic terms. For example, the stakeholder objective of confining flame damage to the compartment of origin could be translated into preventing flashover conditions in the room of fire origin (deterministic) or reducing the probability of flashover to less than a threshold value (probabilistic).

6.2.2 Targets The process of developing quantifiable design objectives should focus on target(s). A target includes the building, compartment, process, or occupant that is protected in order to meet a specific stakeholder objective. For example, the following could be targets: the occupants of the facility (for a life safety fire protection objective); products or valuable equipment in a warehouse (for a property protection objective); a critical production or manufacturing process (for a continuity of operations objective); or water supply and wetlands (for an environmental objective).

6.2.3 Design Objectives Design objectives serve as the benchmarks against which the predicted performance of a trial design will be evaluated using performance criteria expressed in engineering terms, as described in Chapter 7. Appendix B shows example fire protection goals, stakeholder objectives, and design objectives.

Notes

1. *NFPA 5000®*, *Building Construction and Safety Code®*, 2006 edition, National Fire Protection Association, Quincy, MA.

2. *International Code Council Performance Code*, International Code Council, Falls Church, VA, 2003.

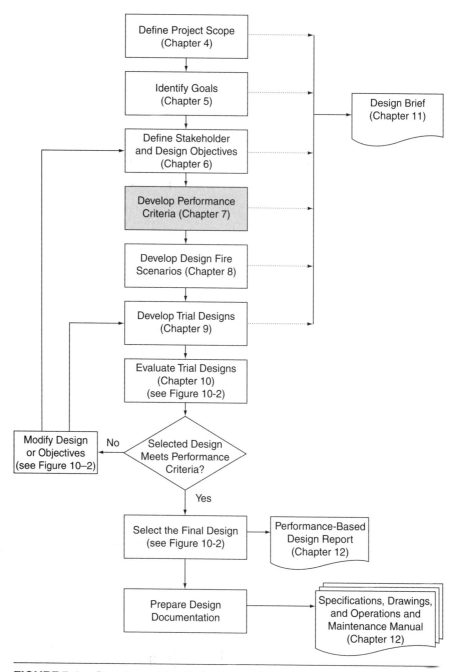

FIGURE 7-1 Overview of the Performance-Based Process, Developing Performance Criteria

CHAPTER 7

Developing Performance Criteria

7.1 General

7.1.1 Definition of Performance Criteria

After stakeholder and design objectives have been established, the next step in the performance-based design process requires selection of performance criteria associated with meeting the design objectives, as shown in Figure 7-1. These criteria will be used to evaluate the trial designs. Performance criteria are threshold values, bounded ranges of threshold values, or distributions of expected performance that are used to develop and evaluate trial designs for a given design situation. Performance criteria might include temperatures of materials, gas temperatures, smoke concentration or obscuration levels, carboxyhemoglobin (COHb) levels, and radiant flux levels. Human response in terms of decision, reaction, and movement times can vary over a range of values. In order to evaluate the adequacy of an egress system design with respect to human exposure criteria, it is necessary to select or assume values for calculation purposes. The rationale for assumptions regarding human behavior should be carefully documented. For example, performance criteria could include values for thermal radiation exposure (kW/m^2) or gas (air) temperature. Other types of performance criteria include concentration of toxic gases (ppm), distance of the smoke layer above the floor (m), visibility (m), or other measurable or calculable parameters. Examples of stakeholder objectives, design objectives, and performance criteria are provided in Appendix B.

7.1.2 Relationship of Performance Criteria to Design Objectives

More than one performance criterion might be required to adequately evaluate a design objective. In addition, more than one value could be required to adequately describe a performance criterion. For example, essential personnel might be required to delay their evacuation to secure an industrial process and therefore experience less tenable conditions than nonessential personnel, who would evacuate sooner. If fire safety engineers determine that delayed evacuation is necessary, they should decide whether the essential personnel, who will delay their evacuation, must be provided with special equipment and training or the facility must be designed with a "defend in place" capability.

7.1.3 Hazard Levels

When defining performance criteria, it is important to note that it is impossible to achieve a completely hazard- or risk-free environment. Additionally, as the level of acceptable hazard or risk decreases, the costs associated with achieving those decreasing levels of risk typically increase.

7.1.4 Evaluation Methodologies

In establishing performance criteria, the engineer should consider whether a valid method exists to evaluate a particular criterion. Evaluation methodologies are discussed in Chapters 9 and 10.

7.2 Translation of Design Objectives into Performance Criteria

Performance criteria are established from the design objectives as developed by the engineer, based on the objectives of the stakeholders and any applicable building regulations. The design objectives are stated in engineering terms, but lack the full specificity of performance criteria. The specificity of performance criteria enables comparison of fire damage with the results of analytical hazard, risk assessment, or fire effects modeling. Performance criteria must be crafted to reflect the intent of the objectives and must be quantitative measures of the consequences of fire that must be avoided in order to fulfill stakeholder objectives. As such, performance criteria generally take the form of damage indicators. It is not necessary that the means of preventing the damage be known at this stage, but a complete understanding of the acceptable limits of damage and injury must be well understood. If the engineer develops the performance criteria, the damage indicators utilized should come from technical documents and their selection should be thoroughly explained to and documented for stakeholders. Some performance criteria could also be set by applicable performance-based codes.[1,2,3]

7.3 Establishment of Specific Performance Criteria

7.3.1 Reference Material

Establishing specific numerical performance requirements for the universe of design situations is beyond the scope of this document. References in Appendix A can be useful in setting performance criteria. Additional references should be used as appropriate. The following paragraphs identify areas in which performance criteria is often needed.

7.3.2 Life Safety Criteria

Life safety criteria address survivability of persons exposed to fire and its products. The performance criteria might vary depending on the physical and mental condition of the occupants and the length of time of expected exposure. Whenever possible, minimum criteria related to life safety should be established for different segments of the population by a consensus of knowledgeable experts, not by individual engineers. For situations in which an individual engineer establishes the life safety criteria, the technical bases for the selected criteria should be documented and subjected to technical review. Understanding human behavior in fire situations is an important part of establishing and evaluating performance criteria.[4]

7.3.2.1 Thermal Effects on Human Beings Analysis of thermal effects includes a threshold injury value and the exposure time to reach the threshold for a given scenario. Injury can result from exposure to thermal radiation[5,6,7] from flames or heated gases. Radiation can also result in ignition of clothing.

7.3.2.2 Toxicity Toxic effects result from inhalation exposure to products of combustion.[7,8,9] Toxic effects on humans may include reduced decision-making capacity and impaired motor activity leading to temporary or permanent incapacitation or death. Analysis of these effects includes a threshold damage value and the exposure time to reach the threshold. Effects may vary depending on the age, health, and activity level of those exposed. The increased temperature in a fire environment can result in rapid breathing and thus faster uptake of toxins.

7.3.2.3 Visibility   Visibility through smoke can affect the ability of occupants to safely exit a building or portion thereof.[7,10] The factors that affect visibility include the optical density in the path of vision and the physiological effects on the eyes.[11] Low light levels can also affect occupants' ability to egress.

7.3.3 Non-Life Safety Criteria

Non-life safety criteria address issues relating to damage thresholds for property. Damage thresholds can relate to exposure to thermal energy resulting in ignition or unacceptable damage. Thresholds can also take into consideration acceptable exposure to smoke aerosols and particulate or corrosive combustion products. In some cases, unacceptable damage might result from very small exposure levels.

7.3.3.1 Thermal Effects on Structures   Thermal effects can include melting, charring, and deformation or ignition of objects or materials, including building construction. Factors contributing to thermal effects can include the following:[5,12,13,14]

- Transmission of energy (convection, conduction, and radiation)
- Distance of the target from the source
- Geometry of the source and the target
- Material conductivity, density, and heat capacity
- Physical characteristics of the target
- Ignition temperature of the target

7.3.3.2 Fire Spread   The spread of fire by progressive ignition should be considered. Factors affecting fire spread include the geometry and orientation of the burning surfaces (horizontal versus vertical) as well as the surface area to mass ratio of the fuels involved.[15] Ventilation and airflow affect fire spread.[14,15] Fire spread can affect life safety, in that rapid fire spread can impair occupant egress.

7.3.3.3 Smoke Damage

Smoke damage occurs through deposition of smoke aerosols and particulate or corrosive combustion products.[13] The damage threshold depends on the sensitivity of the target to damage. Some works of art, such as paintings, have very low thresholds, whereas others such as statuary have higher thresholds. Many targets such as electronics are sensitive to corrosive products at low levels.

7.3.3.4 Fire Barrier Damage and Structural Integrity

Loss of fire barrier integrity can result in damage from extension of heat and smoke. Factors affecting fire barrier integrity include failure of opening protection devices to operate and the presence of improperly protected penetrations in fire barriers. Minimal acceptable performance of fire barriers in terms of potential for extension will depend on the sensitivity of targets to heat and smoke. Structural collapse[16,17,18] is an issue in both life safety and property protection. The stability of a structure is important for occupants during the time necessary for egress and for emergency responders during rescue and suppression activities.

7.3.3.5 Damage to Exposed Properties

It could be necessary to develop performance criteria to prevent or limit damage or fire spread to exposed properties. The mechanism of damage can be thermal or smoke. Factors such as separation distance, material flammability characteristics, the resistance of exposing surfaces, and geometry are important considerations. Clearance of structures from wildland fire-prone materials might also be a criterion in some areas.

7.3.3.6 Damage to the Environment

It could be necessary to develop performance criteria to protect the environment by limiting the effluent associated with fire suppression systems and fire fighting operations or by confining or limiting the release of combustion products.

Notes

1. NFPA *101*®, *Life Safety Code*®, 2006 edition, National Fire Protection Association, Quincy, MA.

2. *International Building Code*, International Code Council, Falls Church, VA, 2003.

3. *NFPA 5000*®, *Building Construction and Safety Code*®, 2006 edition, National Fire Protection Association, Quincy, MA.

4. *Engineering Guide—Human Behavior in Fire*, Society of Fire Protection Engineers, Bethesda, MD, 2003.

5. *Engineering Guide to Assessing Flame Radiation to External Targets from Liquid Pool Fires*, Society of Fire Protection Engineers, Bethesda, MD, 1999.

6. *Engineering Guide to Predicting 1st and 2nd Degree Skin Burns*, Society of Fire Protection Engineers, Bethesda, MD, 1999.

7. Purser, D.A. "Toxicity Assessment of Combustion Products," *The SFPE Handbook of Fire Protection Engineering*, 3rd Edition, National Fire Protection Association, Quincy, MA, 2002.

8. Gann, R., et al. "International Study of the Sublethal Effects of Fire Smoke on Survivability and Health (SEFS): Phase I Final Report," NIST Technical Note 1439, National Institute of Standards and Technology, Gaithersburg, MD, 2001.

9. "Life Threat from Fires—Guidance on the Estimation of Time Available for Escape Using Fire Data," ISO TS 13571, International Standards Organization, Geneva, 2002.

10. Bryan, J.L. "Behavioral Response to Fire and Smoke," *The SFPE Handbook of Fire Protection Engineering*, 3rd Edition, National Fire Protection Association, Quincy, MA, 2002.

11. Mulholland, G.W. "Smoke Production and Properties," *The SFPE Handbook of Fire Protection Engineering*, 3rd Edition, National Fire Protection Association, Quincy, MA, 2002.

12. Kanury, A.M. "Flaming Ignition of Solid Fuels," *The SFPE Handbook of Fire Protection Engineering*, 3rd Edition, National Fire Protection Association, Quincy, MA, 2002.

13. Tewarson, A. "Generation of Heat and Chemical Compounds in Fires," *The SFPE Handbook of Fire Protection Engineering*, 3rd Edition, National Fire Protection Association, Quincy, MA, 2002.

14. Drysdale, D. *An Introduction to Fire Dynamics*, 2nd Edition, John Wiley & Sons, 1999.

15. Quintiere, J.Q. "Surface Flame Spread," *The SFPE Handbook of Fire Protection Engineering*, 3rd Edition, National Fire Protection Association, Quincy, MA, 2002.

16. Milke, J. "Analytical Methods for Determining Fire Resistance of Steel Members," *The SFPE Handbook of Fire Protection Engineering*, 3rd Edition, National Fire Protection Association, Quincy, MA, 2002.

17. Fleishmann, C., & Buchanan, A. "Analytical Methods for Determining Fire Resistance of Concrete Members," *The SFPE Handbook of Fire Protection*

Engineering, 3rd Edition, National Fire Protection Association, Quincy, MA, 2002.

18. White, R. "Analytical Methods for Determining Fire Resistance of Timber Members," *The SFPE Handbook of Fire Protection Engineering*, 3rd Edition, National Fire Protection Association, Quincy, MA, 2002.

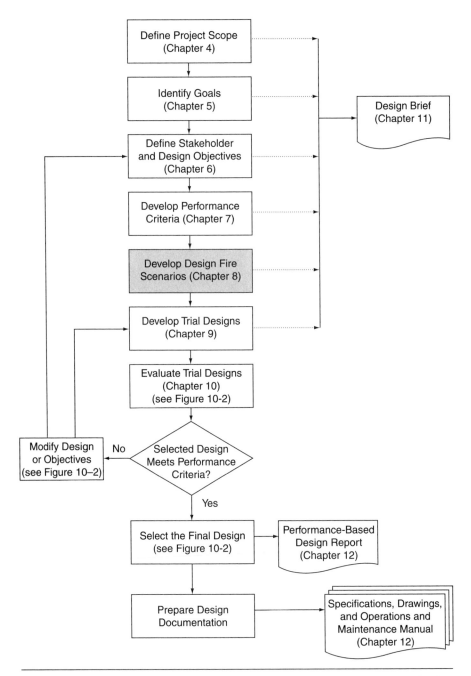

FIGURE 8-1 Overview of the Performance-Based Design Process, Developing Design Fire Scenarios

CHAPTER 8

Developing Design Fire Scenarios

8.1 General

Once the performance criteria have been established, the engineer needs to focus on the fire exposures and the development and analysis of design alternatives to meet the criteria. The analysis entails the consideration of a wide range of possible fire scenarios, with a selected group of scenarios serving as the design fire scenarios. Figure 8-1 illustrates how developing design fire scenarios fits into the overall Performance-Based design process.

After specific design fire scenarios are established, then various design alternatives can be developed into trial designs and evaluated to determine whether the performance criteria will be successfully met by the trial design for the design fire scenarios, as shown in Figure 8-2. (Chapter 9 discusses developing design fire scenarios into trial designs, and Chapter 10 presents the evaluation of trial designs.)

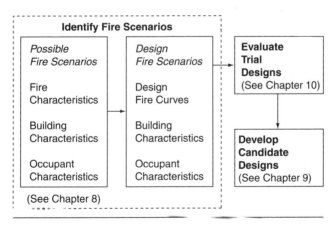

FIGURE 8-2 Process for Identifying, Developing, and Evaluating Fire Scenarios

The process of identifying possible fire scenarios and developing them into design fire scenarios consists of several steps:

1. Identify possible fire scenarios (Section 8.2)
2. Define design fire scenarios, a subset of the possible fire scenarios (Section 8.4)
3. Quantify the design fire scenarios

8.2 Identification of Possible Fire Scenarios

8.2.1 The Purpose of Fire Scenarios

Fire scenarios describe a sequence of possible events and set of conditions that describe the development of fire and the spread of combustion products throughout a building or part of a building. Fire scenarios describe factors critical to the outcome of fires, such as fire protection features, ignition sources, the nature and configuration of the fuel, fire characteristics, ventilation, characteristics and locations of occupants, and conditions of the supporting structure and other equipment. A fire scenario can also include circumstances preceding ignition to the extent that is necessary to help describe subsequent events.

A fire scenario represents one of a set of fire conditions that are thought to be threatening to a building, its occupants, and/or its contents. This description should therefore address the state of the building, its contents, and its occupants at the time of ignition and resultant fire.

Possible fire scenarios form the basis for design fire scenarios, which in turn are used to evaluate trial designs. See Appendix D for an example of a possible fire scenario.

8.2.2 Factors Affecting Fire Development

For a given possible fire scenario, many factors can affect fire development, including the following:

- Form of ignition source
- Type of fuel first ignited
- Secondary fuels ignited and fire spread
- Location of fire
- Effects of compartment geometry on fire development
- Whether doors and windows are initially open or closed, and at what time in the possible fire scenario they are open or closed

- Ventilation, whether natural (i.e., doors and windows) or mechanical (i.e., HVAC, etc.)
- Type of construction and interior finish materials
- Form of intervention (i.e., occupants, fire suppression systems, the fire department, etc.)

8.2.3 Use of Fire Scenario Characteristics

The subsections that follow outline a series of steps for using fire scenario characteristics.

8.2.3.1 *Defining Scenario Components* Prior to developing a possible fire scenario, it is necessary to gather various pre-fire characteristics of the specific building and the building's occupants or assume that these pre-fire characteristics exist (see Section 8.2.3.2). This information includes the chance of fire occurring, how it could develop and spread, and its potential to cause damage to the occupants, structure, and contents. This information will also be used as input variables in Chapter 9, "Developing Trial Designs." Therefore, each scenario should define three components: fire characteristics, building characteristics, and occupant characteristics.

8.2.3.2 *Making Assumptions* During design fire scenario development, it is possible that some information on pre-fire characteristics may be unavailable. It could therefore be necessary to make explicit assumptions to address such points in the analysis and document these assumptions. A sensitivity analysis (see 10.5.6.2) should be carried out to determine the assumptions that are likely to be particularly influential.

The following provides an overview regarding some of the information that should be included when characterizing possible design fire scenarios. Additional information is provided in Section 8.5.

8.2.3.3 *Building Characteristics* Building characteristics describe the physical features, contents, and ambient environment of the building. Building characteristics can affect the evacuation of occupants, growth and spread of a fire, and the movement of products of combustion. Therefore, building characteristics need to be detailed when developing fire scenarios.[1,2]

Building characteristics include the following:

- Architectural features
- Structural components
- Fire protection systems

- Building services and processes
- Building operations
- Characteristics of emergency responder response
- Environmental factors

For further information on building characteristics, see Section 8.5.2.

8.2.3.4 *Defining Occupant Characteristics*   Occupant characteristics need to be defined in order to determine the ability of occupants to respond and evacuate during an emergency. Thus, the following should be considered in the development of each possible fire scenario:[1,2]

- Number of occupants
- Distribution throughout building
- Alertness (sleeping, awake, etc.)
- Commitment
- Focal point
- Physical and mental capabilities
- Role
- Familiarity
- Social affiliation
- Physical and physiological condition
- Training

The engineer should realize that it is important to distinguish between factors that might be directly relevant to occupant behavior and escape (e.g., mobility) and factors that could be indirect indicators for direct factors (e.g., age, sex).

Section 8.5.3 provides additional information on occupant characteristics.

8.2.3.5 *Defining Fire Characteristics*   Fire characteristics describe the history of a fire scenario, which includes the following:

- Ignition sources
- Growth rate
- Flashover
- Full development
- Decay
- Extinction

- Location
- Duration

The engineer should perform a thorough review of the potential and typical fuel packages and ignition sources for the building. It is often difficult to obtain specific information about building contents (i.e., furniture, stored materials, etc.) during the design stages of a project; however, a thorough attempt should be made to understand what combustibles will be in the building or space. If assumptions are made regarding specific burning characteristics of materials, they should be documented and incorporated into final project specifications (such as architectural furniture specifications, if necessary). After the engineer has performed this review of the potential fuel packages and ignition sources that may be present, the engineer should select the technical input related to the fire characteristics to be used for the design analysis. The technical bases for the design fire(s) should be documented and reviewed by qualified personnel. To the extent possible, if standardized design fire data exists, it should be used if it is applicable to the specific situation being assessed. For additional information, see Section 8.5.4.

8.2.3.6 Modifications Where trial designs do not successfully meet the performance criteria for the respective design fire scenarios, it is possible to go back and revise the occupant, building, or fire characteristics. It is typically the building characteristics that are modified when the trial designs are reevaluated. Although it is possible to modify the occupant and fire characteristics, these types of modifications can impose significant requirements or limitations on various aspects of the occupants as well as the building's function. As with all aspects of performance-based design, findings should be properly documented.

8.3 Tools Used in Identifying Possible Fire Scenarios

There are a number of analysis techniques available that can be used to identify possible fire scenarios; some of these techniques are described in the following sections.

8.3.1 Failure Modes and Effects Analysis (FMEA)

Failure Modes and Effects Analysis (FMEA)[3] is used to systematically study possible failure modes of individual components and the results of each failure, either on the system in general or on other components of the system.[4,5]

FMEA originated in the aerospace industry and is used extensively in nuclear applications. However, the technique can also be generalized to assist in the development of possible fire scenarios in a variety of design applications.

A typical FMEA analysis first identifies the items to be studied. Next, the failure modes for each item are listed. A typical list of failure modes includes spark/arc, overheat, leak, rupture, loss of electrical power, or improper control signal input.

For each failure mode, a cause of the failure is then determined. For example, rupture could be due to overpressurization, physical damage, or poor workmanship. The analysis continues, then, to identify the possible effects of each failure. The effects of a rupture obviously depend on what is released. If the material released is a combustible or flammable liquid, the effects can vary depending on a number of factors. For example, in the absence of an ignition source, the release could be merely a pollution or clean up problem. However, if a competent ignition source is present, a fire can result. If the rupture is due to overpressurization during an existing fire, the effect could be a substantially increased growth rate and spread of the fire.

In the process of carrying out a FMEA, it is also useful to assign a rank or criticality level to the particular set of failure modes and effects being studied. The criticality value can consider not only the seriousness of the effect but also the likelihood that the particular failure mode can occur. Events that have a low frequency of occurrence but a very serious effect can be more critical than events that occur frequently but are of little consequence (unless those events affect the system in such a way as to create another failure mode that leads to a greater effect).

8.3.2 Failure Analysis

Failure analysis[4] as used in engineering is the discipline of studying failures to determine the mechanisms by which the failures occurred and to develop means to prevent such failures from occurring in the future. The American Society of Civil Engineers (ASCE) Technical Council on Forensic Engineering defines failure as "an unacceptable difference between expected and observed performance." For example, applying that concept to fire protection, a "fire failure" can be considered an event resulting in unacceptable deaths, injuries, or other losses.

Traditionally, failure analysis has been carried out after a failure occurred. Failure analysis can, however, also be a part of the analysis and design process and can be used to anticipate failures that might compromise the expected performance of a fire protection design. Failure analysis applied during the analysis and design process is used to identify causes of potential failure, identify contributing factors, and evaluate expected system performance.

Failures of fire protection systems can result from the following: design, material, manufacturing or construction, and maintenance.

The analytical tools described elsewhere in this section are useful in identifying possible failure modes for fire safety design.

See Appendix D for an example application of failure analysis.

Failure analysis, then, can be an important tool in developing reliable fire protection design. Failures are much easier to prevent before they occur than they are to control after.

8.3.3 "What if?" Analysis

"What if?" analysis[5] is a simplified technique that involves asking what happens if a particular failure or event occurs. The answer will be an opinion based on the available knowledge of the stakeholders answering the question. The process can be enhanced by brainstorming among multiple stakeholders.

8.3.4 Historical Data, Manuals, and Checklists

As a starting point for the analysis of an existing facility, historical fire incident data[6] for that facility and associated processes or equipment can be reviewed for past scenarios. When a new project is involved, similar occupancy, process, or equipment-related fire statistics for the "general population" could be studied to identify common fire causes as well as other information. However, the scarcity of the data needed for assigning probabilities can limit this approach for conducting performance-based design for a specific project.

Operational manuals and checklists for processes or equipment can be studied to identify potential fire causes as part of the consideration of possible fire scenarios. The study can be accomplished by looking for warnings, cautions, and operational sequences that could lead to a fire if not followed. It should be noted that manuals and checklists might not identify all the possible fire cause or loss scenarios and should be reviewed with the objective of gaining a general understanding to use as a basis for asking questions either of the stakeholder or other resources.

8.3.5 Relevant Statistical Data

When developing scenarios, it can be useful to review statistical data.[7] Although it might not be appropriate to rely entirely on statistical information on fires in similar occupancies with similar fuel loads, past fire histories can provide some very useful input by identifying potential failures of various items, as well as frequencies and severities of fires. It should also be kept in mind when reviewing statistical data that not all foreseeable fire events will appear in the statistical data.

Fire experience data can also be useful in defining high-challenge scenarios. High-challenge scenarios can be defined as those with high historical severity, such as high rates of death per fire. See Appendix C for additional guidance on the use of statistical data to choose possible fire scenarios.

8.3.6 Other Analysis Methods

Several other analysis tools exist that can be used. These include engineering checklists, hazard indices, Hazards and Operability studies (HAZOPS), preliminary hazards analysis (PHA), fault tree analysis (FTA), event tree analysis (ETA), cause consequence analysis, and reliability analysis.

8.3.7 Input from Stakeholders

Stakeholder input can be utilized to establish building characteristics based on plans. Occupant characteristics and fire characteristics can be based on the expected use of the structure. In some cases, the stakeholders can provide guidance to the development of fire scenarios for a building based on the judgment of potential fuels or hazards or a survey of conditions.

8.4 Definition of a Design Fire Scenario

Given the large number of possible fire scenarios for a performance-based design project, it is usually necessary to reduce the possible fire scenarios to a manageable number of credible design fire scenarios that adequately represent the fire hazards. Generally, the broad range of fire scenarios can be filtered into representative design fire scenarios using various methodologies as discussed in this section, by reviewing information presented in certain codes and standards, such as NFPA *101®*, *Life Safety Code®*, and *NFPA 5000®*, *Building Construction and Safety Code®*, or through engineering judgment.

Where calculation methodologies are to be implemented, two general approaches are available: probabilistic and deterministic. Each design fire scenario (which needs to be quantified in engineering terms) is part of a broader scenario group and is meant to be representative of that group. The scenario groups should collectively include the range of potential fire scenarios; this is one of the ways in which some measure of risk can be developed.

8.4.1 Probabilistic Approaches

A probabilistic approach typically deals with the likelihood that a fire will occur and the resultant outcome if a fire does occur. The decision on whether to select a given possible fire scenario as a design fire scenario is influenced by grouping scenarios that are similar. Grouped sets of scenarios can potentially be eliminated from further evaluation if the stakeholders agree that the risk or outcome is acceptable.

8.4.1.1 Probabilities

The likelihood that a specific outcome can occur can be assigned a numerical value between zero and one. Zero indicates that the event cannot occur, whereas one indicates that the event is certain to occur. The probability of a specific outcome, A, can be estimated from the following:

$$P_A = \frac{n_A}{N}$$

where n_A is the number of ways that outcome A can occur, and N is the total possible outcomes.[6]

A conditional probability involves two defined events (e.g., events A and X). $P[A|X]$ represents the conditional probability of event A given event X: this is the probability of A occurring given that event X has already taken place.[7]

Typically, for fire protection analysis the outcome is either pass or fail. The probability that a protective feature would fail to control the fire given that a fire has occurred could be P_{fail}. The probability of successful fire control given that a fire has occurred could be $P_{success}$. Since these probabilities require an event prior to their occurrence, they are referred to as conditional probabilities. For further information, consult the notes.[7,8]

A probabilistic approach could use the information in outlined in Sections 8.4.1.2 through 8.4.1.4 as a source of data for assigning probabilities or frequencies to specific events.

8.4.1.2 Statistics and Historical Information

8.4.1.2.1 Fire Statistics Fire statistics include statistics that identify the most likely areas of ignition, items first ignited, and the likelihood of fire spread beyond the room of fire origin. Fire statistics can be national or local, but usually are applicable to a specific occupancy classification and type of building.[9] If there is a large enough database available, it might also be possible to assign values for the frequency of occurrence of scenarios and establish a relative ranking. This process can result in a detailed risk analysis.

8.4.1.2.2 History History includes historical data from fires for a particular existing building or group of buildings or for similar types of equipment, contents, and so on.

8.4.1.2.3 Fire Frequency The fire frequency is the number of times a fire occurs within a specified time interval. Fire frequency is usually measured in fires per year or events per year. Thus, if the fire frequency for a multi-room fire is stated to be 5E-4 fires/year, the expectation is that a fire involving two or more rooms occurs every 2000 years. In practice, the two-room fire can occur after this period or it could occur next week.

8.4.1.2.4 Fire Initiation Frequency The fire initiation frequency might be based on the building floor area[10] or use. See appendix D for an example using building floor area fire initiation frequencies.

8.4.1.3 Hazard and Failure Analysis
In order to determine fire scenarios, a systematic analysis of the modes of failure and the fire hazards created for the specific occupancy could be used. The analysis occurs more often for industrial premises where HAZOP, Cause Consequence, Failure Modes and Effects Analysis (FMEA), event trees, and fault trees can be used to develop scenarios.

8.4.1.4 System Availability and Reliability

8.4.1.4.1 Fire Protection System Availability Fire protection systems are not always operational. When establishing a fire frequency estimate, the concept of availability should be addressed. An entity (e.g., a fire protection system) is available only when in a state to perform a required function under given conditions at a given instant in time exists.[7] Typically, for fire protection purposes, the "given instant in time" is when a fire starts. If a fire detection system has been inadvertently left out of service after completion of maintenance and a fire occurs, the detection system is, by definition, unavailable. Probabilities can be developed for evaluation of system availability.

8.4.1.4.2 Fire Protection System Reliability Fire protection systems do not always perform as designed or intended. When they fail, the results can be catastrophic. Thus, it is very important that the reliability of fire protection systems be understood and that it be part of the design fire scenario selection. Reliability is the measure that the system will perform as designed or intended.

Sometimes, the availability and reliability are reported or derived as a composite value. When this is the case, the reference value should be explicit in presenting this approach.

8.4.1.4.3 System Availability and Reliability in Existing Building Analyses When developing design fire scenarios for the performance-based analysis of existing buildings, the availability and reliability of all fire protection systems that are in place at the time of the analysis, passive or active, should be considered. Such analysis is especially important when a design fire scenario relies on the successful operation of an installed system (see also Section 8.5.2, "Building Characteristics"). For example, if an existing building has automatic fire detection and notification systems installed throughout, certain assumptions can be made during scenario development relative to activation of the detection system and notification of building occupants. However, these assumptions should consider the likelihood that the system will be available (e.g., no detectors missing, no zones in trouble or shut down) and that the system will operate as expected (e.g., respond as expected to the appropriate fire signature, provide alarm signaling that can be readily heard by building occupants and recognized as a fire alarm signal). (See also Section 8.5.3.) Similar analysis can be appropriate for passive systems that might have been compromised at some point during occupancy of the building (e.g., holes in fire or smoke barriers, damaged or missing door closing devices). Analysis of system availability and system reliability is not required when existing fire protection systems are not considered during the scenario development process. At other times, the system availability and system reliability will be addressed as part of evaluating trial design options (see Chapter 10).

8.4.1.5 *Risk*   A total risk for a building or a facility is a sum of risks associated with possible scenarios. The risk associated with a scenario is a product of the consequences of the scenario and its expected frequency of occurrence (see Appendix E, "Risk Analysis"). Consequences can include occupant death, monetary loss, business interruption, and environmental damage, and they are the consequences associated with an initiating event for a scenario of interest. The frequency of occurrence might be an estimate, usually based on statistics, of how often the initiating event for a scenario can occur.

When considering risk as the basis for cost-benefit analysis, it might be possible to convert risk into equivalent dollars, which in turn allows different types of risks to be compared (e.g., death or injury, monetary loss, business interruption, environmental damage, etc.). This type of analysis can be extremely difficult, however, because of difficulties in establishing a socially acceptable value for a life lost. See Appendices D and E for example applications of this concept.

8.4.2 Deterministic Approach

The deterministic approach relies on analysis or judgment based on physics and chemistry, or correlations developed from testing to predict the outcome of a fire.

Fire scenarios can be evaluated for use as design fire scenarios by estimating whether a given scenario can produce effects that exceed the performance criteria. Those scenarios that do not exceed the performance criteria or are bounded by other design fire scenarios need not be used to evaluate trial designs.

In a deterministic analysis, one or more possible fire scenarios can be developed as design fire scenarios that are representative of potential worst credible fires in a particular building. They can include smoldering and rapidly developing flaming fires. The central challenge in scenario selection is finding a manageable number of fire scenarios that are sufficiently diverse and representative. Finding a representative sample of scenarios ensures that if the design is safe for those scenarios, then it should be safe for all scenarios, except those specifically excluded as too unrealistically severe or too unlikely to be fair tests of the design.

For deterministic design, the frequency of the possible fire scenario does not need to be evaluated. Each design fire scenario should be evaluated separately and they cannot be combined.

The analytical models and analytical methods discussed in Appendix F can be used to determine whether the scenarios would result in unacceptable outcomes.

Implied risk represents the unstated assumptions that the stakeholders have tacitly decided are an acceptable risk. Every trial design is intended to successfully prevent a fire from exceeding the performance criteria. Thus, all fires that can occur in a facility while the fire protection systems are functional and that do not exceed the severity of the design fire curve will not exceed the performance criteria. Those fires that develop more quickly, have a higher heat release rate, or otherwise exceed the severity of the design fire scenario can exceed the performance criteria. This potential illustrates the importance of selecting an appropriate design fire scenario.

8.4.3 Information from Codes and Standards

In recent years, a number of building regulations have been developed around the world to specifically address performance-based design concepts. Some of these documents provide specific information about the types of fires to be considered. For example, NFPA *101*[11] provides qualitative information about eight potential fire scenarios to capture some of the potentially relevant fire hazards and to provide for an evaluation of the life safety capabilities of a building.

Because fire conditions are largely dependent on the fire characteristics of a given building, building regulations are limited in the type of information they can provide. For instance, the building's contents, dimensions, and geometry impact the growth and spread of potential fires. Additionally, because the fire conditions must be presented in a quantifiable form, details about them need to be established by the fire protection engineer. As such, building regulations may only provide qualitative descriptions of the types of fire scenarios to be considered.

Information provided by building regulations is likely be limited to general characterizations about the fire, such as its location, the type of fuel, the rate of growth, and the number of fires.

Other codes that address design fires include the *International Building Code*[12] in its specification for design fires to be considered for smoke management systems. The *International Building Code* does allow a rational analysis to be performed if the design fire varies from that specified.

For the *ICC Performance Code*,[13] design fuel loads are dependent on the measurement of performance as well as the use of the structure. Design fuel loads are typically defined in terms of tolerable impacts on buildings and facilities, their contents, and their occupants. For example, a "mild" fire impact to the contents of a computer room may likely be different than a mild fire impact to a manufacturing facility. Thus, a "small" design fire for the computer room may be different than the "small" design fire for the manufacturing facility. In the same manner, a "mild" impact to the contents of both of these occupancies is likely to be different because of the design fire scenarios being different as well as the contents and their susceptibility to damage being different.

By providing this type of information, the range of potential fires to be considered by the design team can be bounded. This information about design fires also facilitates the overall design process and provides a reference for the enforcement authority when considering a proposed solution. However, it is possible that modifications might need to be made.

8.5 Characterizing Design Fire Scenarios

8.5.1 Information Used to Characterize Design Fire Scenarios

This section provides information to assist in quantifying building characteristics, occupant characteristics, and design fire curves for characterizing design fire scenarios, and also provides information that might be necessary for developing possible fire scenarios.

8.5.1.1 Detailed Analysis and Quantification   The significant aspects of the design fire scenarios should be quantified. Often, neither the resources nor the data, such as ignition energy or rate of heat release for each fuel package, is available to quantify every aspect of a design fire scenario. The detailed analysis and quantification should be limited to the most significant aspects, which can include a range of different fire types (including smoldering fires), fire growth rates, and compartment ventilation rates.[2]

A design fire scenario that is highly improbable and too conservative can lead to an uneconomic building design, which can cause the building not to be built or be functional. On the other hand, a design fire scenario developed using a nonconservative approach, e.g., a long incipient phase or a slow rate of fire growth, could lead to a building design in which there is an unacceptably high risk to occupants.

Design fire scenarios are not a description of how the majority of real fires in the building might be expected to behave. Design fire scenarios are the basis used to develop and test trial designs for robustness and, therefore, should present a conservative approach for analysis and determination of required fire safety measures.

8.5.1.2 The Process of Developing Design Fire Scenarios

Since design fire scenarios represent important input into any fire safety design, the stakeholders should agree to them as soon as possible in the design process.

The process of developing a design fire scenario can be a combination of hazard analysis and risk analysis. The hazard analysis identifies potential ignition sources, fuels, and fire development. The risk analysis can include the indicated hazard analysis, while also noting the likelihood of occurrence, either quantitatively or qualitatively, and the severity of the outcomes.

The design fire scenario should be described in sufficient detail to allow quantification of the scenario during scenario development and the evaluation of trial designs (see Chapter 10, "Evaluating Trial Designs").

8.5.1.3 Fire Design Curve

A portion of the characterization of the design fire scenario is establishing a design fire curve. The stages of fire growth and development of a design fire curve that should be reviewed are ignition, growth, flashover, decay, and burnout.[2]

It might not be necessary to quantify the aspects of each stage. For example, if in a performance-based design, the response of an alternative, automatic fire suppression system to standard sprinklers is being examined for equivalence, the design fire scenario can stop at the point of activation of the suppression system or at complete extinguishment.

For each design fire scenario, the agreement of all stakeholders should be attained on the design fire curve.

8.5.2 Building Characteristics

8.5.2.1 Components

Building characteristics describe the physical features, contents, and ambient internal and external environments of the building. Building characteristics can affect the evacuation of occupants, the growth and spread of a fire, and the movement of products of combustion.[1,2] Therefore, the items detailed in the sections that follow might need to be characterized when developing design fire scenarios.

8.5.2.2 Quantification

The quantification of building characteristics can come from a prescriptive-based design option (if they are not part of the performance-based design), from other disciplines, such as mechanical, electrical, architectural, or interior design, or can be quantified as part of a trial design developed in Chapter 9. The extent to which building characteristics need to be quantified is a function of the level of analysis (see Section 10.2). For a subsystem level design, only the factors pertinent to the design need to be quantified. However, for a building performance level design, all the building characteristics probably require quantification.

8.5.2.3 Architectural Features

The architectural features and construction of the compartment(s) of interest, as well as interconnecting compartments that can be affected, might need to be determined. This information includes the following:

- The area and geometry of the compartment(s), ceiling height, and ceiling configuration (i.e., sloped, beams, etc.)
- Interior finish flammability and thermodynamic properties (thermal conductivity, specific heat, density, etc.)
- Construction materials and properties of walls, partitions, floors, and ceilings
- Position, size, and quantity of openings, or areas of low fire resistance in the external envelope that could provide ventilation (windows, doors, etc.)
- Configuration and location of hidden voids (e.g., ceiling, floors, walls, suspended ceilings, raised floors, etc.)
- Number of stories above and below grade
- Location of the building on the site relative to property lines and other buildings or fire hazards
- Interconnections between compartments
- Relationship of hazards to vulnerable points

8.5.2.4 Structural Components

The structural aspects of the building might need to be determined. The following structural aspects should be considered:

- Location and size of load-bearing elements

- Construction material and properties of structural elements (e.g., strength, thermal conductivity, specific heat, reinforcement, characteristics of connections, etc.)
- Protection material characteristics (thickness, thermal conductivity, specific heat, etc.)
- Design structural loads

8.5.2.5 Fuel Load

The fuel load of the building should be estimated. Statistical data is available on the fuel loads for various occupancy types.[14] The extent to which the fuel load is expected to vary over the life of the performance-based design should be considered. Where there is expected to be limited control over the fuel load, a conservative estimate should be developed.

8.5.2.6 Egress Components

Egress components should be determined, including location and capacity of egress routes and remoteness.

8.5.2.7 Fire Protection Systems

For existing buildings, there could already be fire protection systems that should be considered. In addition, some fire protection systems could have already been predetermined, regardless of the analysis, including the following:

- The type of detection system (e.g., smoke detection, ultra violet infra red [UV/IR], or heat detection), if provided, and the characteristics of the detectors (e.g., location of detectors, type of detectors, and response time index [RTI]) should be determined.
- The type of alarm notification (e.g., voice, sounders, strobes), if provided, and minimum sound pressure levels should be determined.
- The type and characteristics of any suppression systems should be determined (e.g., type of suppression, discharge density or concentration, location of discharge devices, activation characteristics such as type of activation or sprinkler activation temperature, and RTI).

8.5.2.8 Building Services and Processes

The location and capacity of building services equipment and processes should be determined with attention to the following elements:

- The location, capacity, and characteristics of ventilation equipment (mechanical versus natural, continually operating, winter and summer differences, etc.)
- Effects on the ambient environment
- Location and capacity of electrical distribution equipment

- Potential ignition sources
- Process manufacturing equipment, which might need evaluation for property damage or business interruption aspects

8.5.2.9 Operational Characteristics   The operational characteristics of the building, including expected occupancy times (typically a function of time of day and day of the week) should be determined.

8.5.2.10 Fire Department Response Characteristics   Considerations regarding the fire department (e.g., response time of fire fighters, accessibility for fire appliances, fire fighter access within the building, equipment, and services) might need to be determined. The location, capability, and response time of the fire department should also be investigated. See Section 9.5.4 for information on quantifying the effects of fire department operations.

8.5.2.11 Environmental Factors   The environmental factors, both inside and outside the compartment of fire origin, should be determined, including the following:

- Interior ambient temperature and humidity range
- Exterior ambient temperature and humidity range
- Ambient sound levels (as affecting alarm audibility)
- Expected wind conditions (as creating pressure differentials or stack effect)

8.5.3 Occupant Characteristics

The following occupant characteristics described in the sections that follow should be considered.

8.5.3.1 Human Behavior[1,15,16]   Human psychology plays an important role in life safety. The possible actions that might be taken following an occupant becoming aware of a fire need to be considered. These include searching for and rescuing family, friends, or pets; collecting valuables or records; and shutting down processes. Other factors include group behavior and fear reactions. A significant amount of research and a number of technical reports are available that should be reviewed regarding human behavior and fire.[16] Occupant response to other nonfire-related threats may also need to be considered, as well as possible changes in response behavior influenced by the events of September 11, 2001.

8.5.3.2 Response Characteristics The response characteristics of the occupants should be estimated. The response characteristics are a function of the following basic occupant characteristics: sensibility, reactivity, mobility, and susceptibility. They should reflect the expected distribution of characteristics of a population appropriate to the use of the building or various areas of the building.

The four basic characteristics—sensibility, reactivity, mobility, and susceptibility—are occupant characteristics of people in buildings. The characteristics are briefly described as follows:

- *Sensibility to physical cues.* The ability to sense the activation of audible and visual notification appliances or discern and discriminate visual, tactile, and olfactory cues in addition to auditory emanations from the fire itself.

- *Reactivity.* The ability to interpret cues correctly and take appropriate action, which could be a function of cognitive capacity, speed of instinctive reaction, or group dynamics. The possible reliability or likelihood of a wrong decision, such as the influence of familiarity with the premises on wayfinding.

- *Mobility.* Speed of movement is a factor determined by individual capabilities, as well as crowding phenomena such as queuing at doorways and reduced travel speeds.

- *Susceptibility to products of combustion.* Metabolism, lung capacity, pulmonary disease, allergies, or other physical limitations that can affect survivability in a fire environment.

Response characteristics could address the following factors that are components of these basic occupant characteristics:

- *Alertness.* Awake or asleep, which can be a function of the time of day

- *Responsiveness.* The ability to sense cues and react

- *Commitment.* The degree to which occupant is committed to an activity underway before the alarm

- *Focal point.* The point at which an occupant's attention might be focused (e.g., to the front of a classroom or to a stage)

- *Physical and mental capabilities.* The ability to sense, respond and react to cues. Physical and mental capabilities can also be related to age or disability

- *Role.* A factor that can determine whether the occupant will lead or follow others

- *Familiarity with the building and evacuation procedures.* A factor that can depend on time spent in a building or participation in emergency training
- *Social affiliation.* A factor that can affect the extent to which an occupant acts or reacts as an individual or as a member of a group
- *Condition.* The physiological and psychological condition of the occupants, which can vary over the course of the fire depending on the exposure to fire and combustion products

8.5.3.3 Occupant Loads

Efforts should be made to obtain accurate occupant load information. Codes typically use occupant load factors that are dependent on occupancy type.[11] However, various types of events, layouts, and so on can impact the actual number of occupants that end up occupying a space over the life of the building.

8.5.3.4 Evacuation Times Predictions[17,18,19,20]

Prediction of the movement of occupants during egress is an essential part of meeting life safety goals. The essential issue here is the estimation or prediction of the time needed for egress. The estimation should include detection, notification time,[21] pre-movement time, movement/travel time, queuing time, travel time within the exit, and discharge time. Also, a number of factors affect egress time, including the number of occupants, distribution throughout the building, response to the notification (or fire alarm), age, health, mental capacity, motivation, and state of wakefulness of the occupants. The availability and level of training of the occupants or the staff, in the case of institutional, assembly, educational, or health care occupancies, is also a factor.

The physical design of the egress system also affects egress time. The physical factors include location, width, and number of egress pathways; and width, tread depth, and riser height and number of stairways; as well as lighting and signage. Changes in width of the egress paths or the intersection of multiple egress paths can result in congestion and slowing of movement. There has also been research and discussion regarding the use of elevators for evacuation that may also need to be considered.[22]

8.5.3.5 Egress Flow

After occupants decide to evacuate, there are methods[18] and computer models available to estimate the flow time through egress paths. Several scenarios should be considered, including varying locations of fires, occupant characteristics, and impacts on exits. The nature of estimating human behavior makes it difficult to accurately quantify the times of key events for the broad population. Therefore, careful attention should be paid to the treatment of uncertainty, as described in Section 10.5.

8.5.4 Quantifying Design Fire Scenarios and Design Fire Curves

8.5.4.1 Fire Development Design fire curves are a vital part of the technical or engineering manifestation of design fire scenarios. Design fire curves are time based and usually establish a relationship between heat release rate and time. Design fire curves have a number of events and stages of development. These are shown in Figure 8-3.[2]

The design fire curve is usually described for a typical room or area of fire origin. Sometimes, only the growth phase or time up to full development or flashover is considered, depending on the design objectives and trial designs being considered.

Suppression might not form part of a performance-based design, and the fire may spread to adjoining rooms or spaces. In such cases, design fire scenarios expressed in terms of heat release rate versus time are required for the subsequent rooms involved. Design fire scenarios expressed in terms of heat release are especially useful when fully developed fires (full room involvement) need to be examined for the effect on the performance of structural elements and compartmentation.

8.5.4.2 Design Fire Curve Stages In any design fire curve that passes through a series of stages, it is often necessary to estimate the time of key stages. These stages can include ignition, growth (pre-flashover), fully developed, flashover, post flashover, decay, and extinguishment.

8.5.4.2.1 Ignition Sources Ignition requires the presence of three items: fuel, oxygen, and an ignition source.[3] Ignition does not occur unless there is sufficient contact time with the source for the fuel to be raised to its ignition temperature given the energy of the ignition source. Because most buildings have fuel sources and oxygen, development of a design fire scenario can

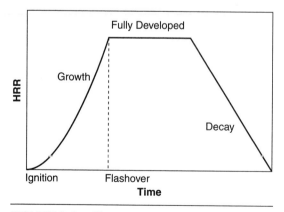

FIGURE 8-3 Characteristics of a Design Fire

require identifying potential ignition sources. When using a deterministic approach the engineer might just assume ignition. In evaluating potential ignition sources, the temperature, energy, time, and area of contact with potential fuels should be considered.

The approach to identifying ignition sources can be general. Ignition sources can be found throughout most parts of a building (e.g., electrical wiring or lighting) or might be located there at some point in the life cycle of the building (e.g., cutting and welding).

Having identified other aspects of a possible scenario, such as a particularly hazardous location, the engineer can use knowledge of potential ignition sources that might exist to establish the importance of the particular scenario.

An ignition with a low frequency of occurrence can result in the greatest loss, and it might need to be considered in the development of possible fire scenarios.

For design purposes, ignition is usually taken as the starting point or origin of the heat release rate $(\dot{Q})$ versus time (t) design fire curve. Prefire situations are worth examining, at least in terms of measures of fire prevention that could be taken in a building to minimize the risk of fires occurring. However, for fire protection engineering purposes, ignition is taken as the beginning of the design fire curve when self-sustaining combustion occurs.

Other initiators can include explosions, earthquakes, or earthquakes followed by fire. In those buildings where an explosion potential exists because of the nature of the occupancy, or for those areas where earthquakes are a significant concern, appropriate consideration should be given to these initiator events.

8.5.4.2.2 Growth (Pre-Flashover) Stage In the growth stage, the worst credible fires can be rapidly developing flaming fires that have little or no incipient phase. However, designs should consider the possibility of scenarios and design fire scenarios with a relatively long smoldering phase that could cause fatalities or damage to critical targets even before established burning.

For smoldering fires, there is little data available. The engineer should therefore choose carefully in developing any specific relationship for the design fire curve heat release rate. For flaming fires, the rate of growth is determined by characteristics of the initial and secondary fuels, as well as the fire's potential to extend beyond the room of origin (i.e., extension potential).

8.5.4.2.3 Initial Fuels After the ignition sources are identified, the characteristics of the initial fuels, or fuel packages, in the vicinity of these sources need to be evaluated.[23]

- *State.* A given fuel can come in various states (i.e., solid, liquid, or gas). Each state can have very different combustion characteristics. A solid block of wood can be difficult to light with a match. Wood shavings can

be easier to light, and if the wood were reduced to dust, it could be ignited by a spark and potentially create an explosion.

- *Type and quantity of fuel.* The development and duration of a fire depends on what is burning and its state. Cellulosic-based materials and
products burn differently than plastics or flammable liquids, producing
different heat release rates, fire growth rates, and products of combustion. The quantity of fuel and its form (surface area to mass ratio) determine how long a fire could potentially burn.

- *Fuel configuration.* The geometrical arrangement of the fuel also influ-
ences the rate of growth and heat release rate of a fire. A wood block
burns very differently from a wood crib because of increased ventilation,
more surface area, and increased radiation feedback between the combustible materials.

- Fuel location. The location of the fuel (i.e., against a wall, in a corner, in
the open, or against the ceiling) will influence the development of the
fire. Fires in the corner of a room or against a wall typically grow faster
than a fire located in the center of a room.[24]

- *Rate of heat release.* The amount of heat released per unit of time depends on the fuel's heat of combustion, the mass loss rate, the amount of
incident heat flux, and the efficiency of combustion.[25] In addition to determining the time taken for the fire to significantly affect its surround-
ings, the rate of heat release can affect the response of combustible items.
The mass loss rate also directly relates to the production rate of smoke,
toxic gases, and other products of combustion.

- *Rate of fire growth.* The rate at which a fire grows is important, as fire
can be time dependent. Fires grow at various rates that depend on the
type of fuel, its configuration, and the amount of ventilation. The faster
a fire develops, the faster the temperature rises, and the faster the products of combustion are produced.[24,25,26,27]

- *Production rate of combustion products (smoke, CO, CO_2, etc.).* Because
of the different compositions of various fuels, as well as how they burn,
the type and quantity of materials generated during combustion vary.
These products will include those that affect not only life safety, such as
quantity of smoke, carbon monoxide, and carbon dioxide, but also those
that affect property and business interruption, such as HCl, that could
damage electronic equipment. Species production rates can be estimated
using species yields, which are representative of the mass of species produced per mass of fuel loss.[25]

8.5.4.2.4 Secondary Fuels As a fire begins to grow in the initial fuel package, it can produce sufficient conductive, convective, and radiant energy to

ignite adjacent fuel packages. Thus, in the development of a design fire scenario, the secondary fuel[3] packages need to be identified and their characteristics defined in order to determine if they will become involved and allow the fire to grow. Ignition of secondary fuels can occur through conduction, convection, radiation, or a combination.[2]

Conduction occurs when the heat in the fire plume is transported through solid materials to the secondary fuel package. Important parameters regarding conduction include temperature of the reaction zone, conductivity, and ignition temperature of the secondary fuel materials.[28,29]

Convection occurs when the fire plume carries heat to the secondary fuel packages. Convection can involve the carrying of embers that can cause piloted ignition. Important parameters regarding convection include the potential for flame impingement from the initial fuel source, temperature of the plume, heat transfer coefficient, and ignition characteristics of adjacent items.

Radiation is typically the main mode of heat transfer to adjacent fuel packages. Important parameters regarding radiation include size of the flame, temperature, emissivity of the flame, absorptivity of the combustible surfaces, the geometric viewing factor between the flames and the combustible surface of the adjacent fuel, and its ignition characteristics.[30]

The factors that need to be identified regarding these secondary fuel packages, in addition to those outlined under Section 8.5.4.2.3, "Initial Fuels," include proximity to initial fuels, amount, and distribution.

8.5.4.2.5 Extension Potential   The potential extension[3] of a fire and its combustion products beyond the compartment or area of origin might also need to be considered. In addition to the fuel loading of the space, the construction features and layout of the compartment need to be analyzed in terms of how the fire and smoke can potentially extend beyond the original space.

A fire and its combustion products can extend to adjacent spaces in several ways, including through openings via radiant energy or continuous fuel packages, through compartment walls via conduction, or through building services such as shafts and HVAC systems. The effects of building HVAC systems should also be considered because they can carry smoke and heat as well as toxic and corrosive products from one location to a location that can also be served by the same system.

Extension potential should be reviewed, not only for fires extending within a building, but also for fires extending over the external surfaces of the building or to adjacent buildings or structures.

8.5.4.2.6 Target locations   When evaluating the expected development and spread of the fire, heat, and products of combustion, the engineer should consider the location of the target items that correspond to stakeholder objectives.

8.5.4.3 Development of Design Fire Curves   For flaming fires scenarios, design fire curves can be developed based on the following items:

- Heat release data on specific individual items likely to be in the building being designed can be aggregated to produce a design fire curve in a theoretical analysis
- Experimental heat release rate (HRR) data from items burned under a furniture calorimeter, in a corner burn test, or inferred from cone calorimeter data
- Full-scale test from mock-up sections of an actual building
- Generic curves for particular growth rates
- A fire growth model that can generate HRR data from fuel package data.

For further information on data sources, see Section 8.5.4.4.

Based on an understanding of the concepts of preflashover fires identified previously, the engineer should quantify the fire heat release rate as part of the design fire curve. The fire growth rate is usually tabulated or drawn as a curve, and it serves as input to analytical equations or fire models to determine key fire safety parameters and times to key stages.

8.5.4.3.1 Flashover   A key stage in fire safety is flashover (e.g., the point at which the rate of heat release, temperature, smoke production, and toxicity of smoke increase rapidly). The avoidance of flashover is often a critical fire protection engineering design objective for life safety and property protection.

The factors that affect whether flashover occurs in an enclosure include the following:[31]

- Surface area of the enclosure (A)
- The area of enclosure openings (A_o)
- The effective height of enclosure openings (H_o)
- Heat release rate
- Ventilation
- Thermal properties of compartment boundaries

Occupant evacuation of the room of fire origin before flashover is essential for life safety. It is important to note that analytically eliminating the chance of flashover does not necessarily prevent fire extension or large-scale fire development. However, flashover does not always occur.

8.5.4.3.2 Fully Developed (Steady or Post-Flashover) Fires   In some design fire scenarios, the design fire might not reach flashover because of the fire occurring in very large volumes or in which there are limitations on avail-

able fuel or combustion air. The fire will reach a peak or steady heat release rate. This peak burning period will last for some period of time, which can be short or extended. The peak heat release rate is typically a factor of the fuel and the burning area.[32]

In some cases, it is assumed that fully developed fires occur with total involvement of the fire enclosure, often leading to spread to other enclosures. This fully developed part of the design fire curve is used by the engineer in a design sense to determine the effect of the following items:

- Radiation through openings and potential ignition of adjoining buildings
- Failure of structural elements that can endanger life safety or cause unacceptable building or contents damage
- Fire spread to other enclosures through convected and radiated heat
- Failure of fire-resisting compartment elements designed to prevent fire spread to other parts of the building

The design fire scenario in the fully developed stage is controlled either by the available ventilation or the fuel available. The engineer should calculate the heat release rate at ventilation control (Q_{vc}) and fuel control (Q_{fc}) and use the most appropriate of the two figures as the peak heat release rate for fully developed fire, as illustrated in Figure 8-4.

The methods and data for establishing the fully developed heat release rate for this stage of the design fire curve can be found in various references.[31] Additional data sources are discussed in Section 8.5.4.4.

For some design situations involving compartmentation or structural fire resistance, the expected duration of the fire might need to be considered.

8.5.4.3.3 Decay and Extinction   Fires decay and eventually burn out after a period of time. Decay can be attributed to depletion of fuel load, lack of

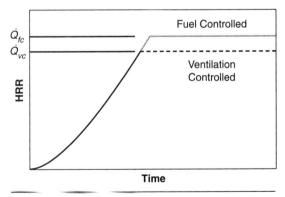

FIGURE 8-4   Ventilation and Fuel Controlled Fires

ventilation, or manual or automatic suppression systems that extinguish the fire. Correlations exist to predict the decay period for some scenarios.[32,33]

8.5.4.4 *Data Sources*

Several methods can be used to define a design fire curve: using published data, fire testing, or calculating a theoretical fire size. In a fire protection engineering design, it can be useful to consider more than one of these methods.

8.5.4.4.1 Technical Literature

When developing a design fire scenario and defining a design fire curve, the use of previously determined and reviewed data is an important tool. There are various sources of heat release rates and associated data (see Appendix A).

8.5.4.4.2 Fire Testing

Fire testing can be used to collect heat release data that might be necessary to develop design fire curves. There are many standard test methods available for the collection of heat release data, ranging from small samples[34,35] to individual pieces of furniture[36,37] to complete room configurations.[38]

8.5.4.4.3 Theoretical Methods

Ideally, actual fire test data would be used when developing the design fire curves for use in a performance-based analysis; however, heat release and associated species generation data might not be available for the specific fuel packages and design fire scenarios being considered. Resource limitations might preclude conducting fire testing. In these cases, the use of theoretical or nominal heat release rate and species generation curves might be necessary.

Empirical correlations for heat release rates have been developed from test data for a number of fuel packages, including flammable liquid pool fires,[39] wood cribs,[40] upholstered furniture,[41] and electrical cable trays.[41] The application of these correlations requires knowledge of material properties, such as heat of combustion, size and configuration of the commodity, and, in some cases, information on ventilation rates.

The heat release rate during the growth phase of a fire can, in many cases, be generically represented by a time-dependent exponential function. One such approach, commonly referred to as a "t^2 fire," is to represent the heat release rate as increasing proportionately to the square of the time since ignition.

In addition, several fire modeling software packages, such as FPETool[42] and HAZARD I[43] contain routines for estimating fire growth curves to represent the cumulative heat release rate due to the burning of multiple fuel packages. These routines require the input of fire growth curves for each fuel package to be considered and information regarding the spatial separation and physical arrangement of the fuels. One or more fuel packages are designated as being initially ignited and the routine determines the resulting fire growth curve from the subsequent ignition of the other fuel packages.

Caution must be exercised when utilizing a theoretical fire growth curve because the resulting fire growth curves are approximations of the anticipated fire conditions. Appropriate conservatism and safety factors, such as selecting a larger than expected heat release rate, might need to be included in the analysis in order to compensate for the uncertainty associated with the theoretical computational methods for developing the fire growth curves (see Section 10.5).

Appendix F provides guidance on the selection of analytical methods.

8.6 Next Steps

In the performance-based design process, fire scenarios are designed as described in this chapter and then trial designs are developed and evaluated. Chapter 9 covers the development of trial designs and Chapter 10 covers their analysis.

Notes

1. BS 7974, "Application of fire safety engineering principles to the design of buildings," BSI, London, 2001.

2. *International Fire Engineering Guidelines*, Australian Building Codes Board, Canberra, ACT, Australia, 2005.

3. Custer, R.L.P., & Meacham, B.J. *Introduction to Performance-Based Fire Safety*, National Fire Protection Association, Quincy, MA, 1997.

4. Hensley, E., & Kumamoto, H. *Reliability Engineering and Risk Assessment*, Prentice-Hall, Englewood Cliffs, NJ, 1981.

5. Hammer, W. *Handbook of System and Product Safety*, Prentice-Hall, Englewood Cliffs, NJ, 1972.

6. Wadsworth, H.M. "Summarization and Interpolation of Data," *Handbook of Statistical Methods for Engineers and Scientists*, ed. H.M. Wadsworth, McGraw-Hill Publishing, New York, 1990.

7. Villemeur, Alain. *Reliability, Availability, Maintainability and Safety Assessment*, John Wiley and Sons, Chichester, UK, 1992.

8. Hall, J. "Probability Concepts," *The SFPE Handbook of Fire Protection Engineering*, 3rd Edition, National Fire Protection Association, Quincy, MA, 2002.

9. Aherns, M., Frazier, P., & Heeschen, J. "Use of Fire Incident Data and Statistics," *Fire Protection Handbook*, 19th Edition, National Fire Protection Association, Quincy, MA, 2003.

10. Coutts, D.A. "Fire Risk Assessment Methodology Generic Event Tree Description (U)," Westinghouse Savannah River Company, Aiken, SC. WSRC-TR-94-0188, 1994.

11. NFPA *101®*, *Life Safety Code®*, 2006 edition, National Fire Protection Association, Quincy, MA.

12. *International Building Code*, International Code Council, Falls Church, VA, 2003.

13. *International Code Council Performance Code*, International Code Council, Falls Church, VA, 2003.

14. CIB, *A Conceptual Approach Towards a Probability Based Design Guide on Structural Fire Safety*. CIB W14 Workshop Report, 1983.

15. Bryan, J. L. "Behavioral Response to Fire and Smoke," *The SFPE Handbook of Fire Protection Engineering*, 3rd Edition, National Fire Protection Association, Quincy, MA, 2002.

16. *Engineering Guide: Human Behavior in Fire*, Bethesda, MD: Society of Fire Protection Engineering, 2003.

17. Proulx, G. "Movement of People: The Evacuation Timing," *The SFPE Handbook of Fire Protection Engineering*, 3rd Edition, National Fire Protection Association, Quincy, MA, 2002.

18. Nelson, H. E., & Mowrer, F.W. "Emergency Movement," *The SFPE Handbook of Fire Protection Engineering*, 3rd Edition, National Fire Protection Association, Quincy, MA, 2002.

19. Shields, J., ed., *Proceedings of the First International Symposium on Human Behavior in Fire*, University of Ulster, 1998.

20. Section 4, Human Behavior in Fire Emergencies, *Fire Protection Handbook*, 19th Edition, National Fire Protection Association, Quincy, MA, 2003.

21. Proulx, G. "Occupant Response to Fire Alarm Signals," *National Fire Alarm Code® Handbook*. National Fire Protection Association, Quincy, MA, 2002.

22. "Emergency Evacuation Elevator Systems Guide," Council on Tall Buildings in Urban Habitat, Chicago, IL, 2004.

23. Bukowski, R. "Fire Hazard Analysis," *Fire Protection Handbook*, 19th Edition, National Fire Protection Association, Quincy, MA, 2003.

24. Zukoski, Kubota & Cetegen. "Entrainment in Fire Plumes," *Fire Safety Journal*, vol. 3, pp. 107–121, 1980.

25. Tewarson, A. "Generation of Heat and Chemical Compounds in Fires," *The SFPE Handbook of Fire Protection Engineering*, 3rd Edition, National Fire Protection Association, Quincy, MA, 2002.

26. McCaffrey, B. "Purely Buoyant Diffusion Flames: Some Experimental Results," National Institute of Standards and Technology, NBSIR 79-1910, 1979.

27. Thomas, P., Hinkley, P., Theobald, C., & Simms, D. "Investigations into the Flow of Hot Gasses in Roof Venting," Fire Research Technical Paper No. 7, HMSO, London, 1963.

28. Drysdale, D.D. *Introduction to Fire Dynamics*, 2nd Edition, John Wiley and Sons, New York, 1999.

29. *NFPA 72®, National Fire Alarm Code®*, Appendix B, National Fire Protection Association, Quincy, MA, 2002.

30. *Engineering Guide: Assessing Flame Radiation to External Targets from Pool Fires*, Society of Fire Protection Engineers, Bethesda, MD, 1999.

31. Walton, W.D., & Thomas, P. "Estimating Temperatures in Compartment Fires," The *SFPE Handbook of Fire Protection Engineering*, 3rd Edition, National Fire Protection Association, Quincy, MA, 2002.

32. *Engineering Guide: Fire Exposures to Structural Elements*, Society of Fire Protection Engineers, Bethesda, MD, 2004.

33. Evans, D. "Sprinkler Fire Suppression Algorithm for HAZARD," NISTIR 5254, National Institute of Standards and Technology, Gaithersburg, MD, 1993.

34. *Standard Test Method for Determining Material Ignition and Flame Spread Properties*, E1321, American Society for Testing and Materials, West Conshohocken, PA, 2002.

35. *Standard Test Method for Heat and Visible Smoke Release Rates for Materials and Products Using an Oxygen Consumption Calorimeter*, E1354, American Society for Testing and Materials, West Conshohocken, PA, 2004.

36. *Standard Test Method for Fire Testing of Upholstered Furniture*, E1537, American Society for Testing and Materials, West Conshohocken, PA, 2002.

37. *Standard Test Method for Fire Testing of Mattresses*, E1590, American Society for Testing and Materials, West Conshohocken, PA, 2002.

38. *Standard Guide for Room Fire Experiments*, E603, American Society for Testing and Materials, West Conshohocken, PA, 2004.

39. Beyler, C. "Fire Hazard Calculations for Large Open, Hydrocarbon Fires," *The SFPE Handbook of Fire Protection Engineering*, 3rd Edition, National Fire Protection Association, Quincy, MA, 2002.

40. Babrauskas, V. "Heat Release Rates," *The SFPE Handbook of Fire Protection Engineering*, 3rd Edition, National Fire Protection Association, Quincy, MA, 2002.

41. Babrauskas, V., & Grayson, S.J., eds. *Heat Release in Fires*, Elsevier Applied Science, New York, NY, 1992.

42. Deal, S. "Technical Reference Guide for FPEtool Version 3.2," NISTIR 5486-1, Building and Fire Research Laboratory, National Institutes of Standards & Technology, Gaithersburg, MD, 1995.

43. Peacock, R., Jones, W., Bukowski, R., & Forney, C. "Technical Reference Guide for the HAZARD I Fire Hazard Assessment Model, Version 1.1," Handbook 146, National Institutes of Standards & Technology, Gaithersburg, MD, 1996.

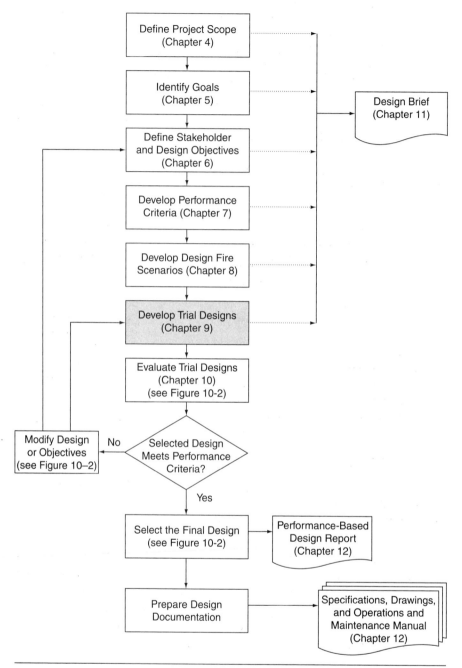

FIGURE 9-1 Overview of the Performance-Based Design Process, Developing Trial Designs

CHAPTER 9

Developing Trial Designs

9.1 General

9.1.1 Definition of Trial Designs

Trial designs characterize the building as well as fire and life safety features. The trial design that is shown in Figure 9-1 is evaluated against the design fire scenarios using the methods described in Chapter 10 to determine if the performance criteria have been satisfied. (See Chapter 8 for information on developing design fire scenarios, Chapter 10 for evaluating trial designs, and Chapter 7 for developing performance criteria.)

9.1.2 Evaluation of Trial Designs

The process of evaluating the trial designs can take a number of iterations with subsequent modification to the trial design until the performance criteria are satisfied. A series of trial designs could be necessary to capture the intent of the overall building design and to adequately evaluate whether the performance criteria have been satisfied. The trial design or the series of trial designs that satisfy the performance criteria become the basis for the building design specifications.

When developing trial designs, the context in which the designs will be evaluated needs to be understood. Trial designs can be evaluated at various levels: for example, at the subsystem level to determine sprinkler activation times; at a system performance level to evaluate a smoke management system; or at a building performance level.

9.1.3 Development of Trial Designs

When developing trial designs, the context in which the designs will be evaluated needs to be understood. Trial designs can be developed with the intent of comparing their performance to that of a design arrangement specified by a building regulation. Developing trial designs in this context could also require selecting building features similar to those of the prescriptive-based design option, but with enhanced capabilities or features.

Alternatively, building features could be selected that provide appropriate safeguards in a different manner. For example, in lieu of extinguishing a fire to mitigate a smoke hazard, venting could be used to purge the smoke. Using prescribed features as a benchmark for comparison, it is possible to demonstrate whether a trial design offers the same level of performance. When comparing the performance of a trial design to that of a code-prescribed solution, the performance criteria against which the trial designs are evaluated could be extracted or otherwise derived from the performance of the systems installed as per code requirements.

9.1.4 Fulfillment of Performance Criteria

Establishing trial designs requires the selection and development of building design features that are expected to fulfill the performance criteria for the selected design fire scenarios. When developing trial designs, consideration needs to be given to a number of factors, including the capabilities, reliability, costs, and maintenance considerations of the design features and systems that are proposed.

With recent world events, trial designs are likely to include features and systems that are intended to protect against threats in addition to accidental fire such as arson, explosion or blast impact, or chemical or biological exposure. Consideration of these additional threats can impact the design of safety features and systems by necessitating an increased level of redundancy or robustness (i.e., redundant water supply feeds, longer duration for emergency power, alternative fire proofing materials, etc.).

9.1.5 Fire Protection Strategies

9.1.5.1   The overall level of fire safety in a building is a function of the interaction of the fire and life safety systems, the response of building occupants, and the reaction of building contents to be protected. Stakeholders, who are familiar with the safety systems, occupants, and contents of the building to be constructed, should provide input to the trial designs to be evaluated.

9.1.5.2   The subsystems that are discussed in this guide include the following:

1. Fire initiation and development (Section 9.2)
2. Spread, control, and management of smoke (Section 9.3)
3. Fire detection and notification (Section 9.4)

4. Fire suppression (Section 9.5)

5. Egress provisions including occupant behavior (Section 9.6)

6. Passive fire protection (Section 9.7)

9.1.5.3   Although each subsystem/component may be evaluated separately, the interactions between subsystems/components must also be determined. For system performance, or building performance evaluations, the interactions between the various subsystems that make up the trial design need to be considered.

9.1.5.4   For any single given design, not all the subsystems described in this guide have to be used. The selection of the combination of subsystems used for any given design is determined by the performance criteria the design is intended to achieve for the specified design fire scenarios.

9.1.6 Methods of Developing Trial Designs

Various methods of achieving a design objective and meeting performance criteria must be considered when developing and evaluating trial designs. These methods will make use of fire protection approaches such as suppression, detection, compartmentation, and material flammability control.

9.1.6.1   NFPA 550, *Guide to the Fire Safety Concepts Tree*,[1] can assist with identifying general approaches and methods for achieving a given design objective. As shown in Figure 9-2, the "Manage fire" branch of the *Fire Safety Concepts Tree* illustrates three approaches to fire management: "Control combustion process," "Suppress fire," and "Control fire by construction." Note that in Figures 9-2 and 9-3, the "or" gate is represented by a "+", and "and" gates are represented by "_". The three approaches shown in Figure 9-2 are separated by an "or" gate to indicate that any one of them can be used.

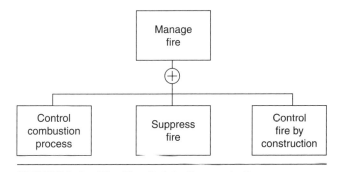

FIGURE 9-2   The Fire Safety Concepts Tree

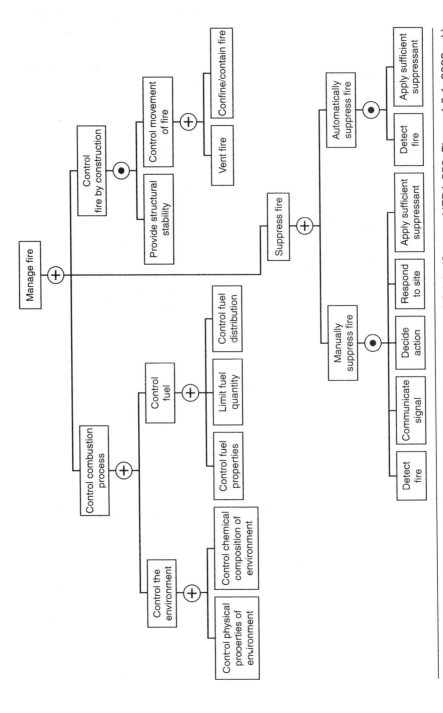

FIGURE 9-3   Limiting the Spread of Flame to the Compartment of Origin (Source: NFPA 550, Figure 4.5.1, 2002 ed.)

As shown in Figure 9-3, each of these three methods—controlling combustion, suppressing the fire, and controlling the fire by construction—is further subdivided until the lowest level of the tree is reached. The courses of action depicted at this lowest level of Figure 9-3 should be considered when developing the components of a trial design. Where courses of action are separated by an "and" gate, the safety features and systems identified are intended to satisfy the individual objective collectively. Where courses of action are separated by "or" gates, it is intended that the individual feature or system satisfy the objective independently.

Some courses of action shown in Figure 9-3 might need to be further broken down to a level not included in the *Fire Safety Concepts Tree.* For example the category entitled "Apply Sufficient Suppressant" could need to be further subdivided depending on what type of suppressant is used, while also considering the fire characteristics and building characteristics. Also, the time associated with agent delivery might need to be considered since the quantity of agent required could be a function of fire size, which is typically a function of time.

As another example, consider the design intent "limit the spread of flame to the compartment of origin." In NFPA 550,[1] limiting the spread of fire to the compartment of origin corresponds to the "Manage fire" branch of the tree (see Figure 9-3). The requirements of the "Manage fire" branch can be met by controlling the combustion process, fire suppression, or controlling the fire by construction. Following the tree to the lower levels yields possible strategies, which can be developed into components of the trial design associated with managing the fire.

9.1.6.2   In addition to using the *Fire Safety Concepts Tree* to determine suitable performance criteria, the methods for developing design fire scenarios, which are identified in Chapter 8, can be used to determine methods of achieving design objectives.

9.1.6.3   When it is necessary for a performance-based design to be "equivalent" to a mandated requirement, such as in a law, regulation, or code, it will be necessary to determine what performance is intended by the mandated or prescriptive requirement. For example, if a stakeholder wants automatic sprinklers or the "equivalent," the fire size at the time of sprinkler operation, the level and distribution of smoke, and other products of combustion must be quantified for the specific building and fire scenario in question. This quantification establishes the base line performance equivalency for alternative designs.

9.1.7 Options for Trial Designs

9.1.7.1   There are several options from which to choose for any given fire protection system. The choice of which subsystems to include in trial designs is dependent in part on the performance criteria developed in Chapter 7, as well as other factors, such as the geometry of the space.

9.1.7.2   Different trial designs should be developed using various combinations of the subsystems identified in 9.1.5.2. The design team should be involved in developing the different combinations of components.

9.1.7.3   The options (subsystems) for trial designs are discussed in Sections 9.2 through 9.7.

9.2 Fire Initiation and Development

9.2.1 Prevention of Ignition

9.2.1.1 Intent   The intent is to reduce the probability (or likelihood) that ignition will occur.

9.2.1.2 Concepts   Prevention of ignition is based on the following concepts:

- *Control Sources.* Ignition sources are controlled in the following three ways:
  - *Removal.* Remove ignition sources from area.
  - *Isolation.* Separate ignition sources from combustibles by physical space.
  - *Management.* Select heat-producing and other equipment that uses intrinsically safe designs.
- *Control Materials.* Selecting materials that are inherently resistant to ignition can control the propensity for ignition. Materials that have a high thermal inertia will be inherently less prone to ignition than materials with a low thermal inertia.[2] For additional information on thermal inertia, see *The SFPE Handbook of Fire Protection Engineering.*[3] Additionally, materials that use fire retardants could be considered; however, the effect of time and wear on the fire retardant and need for maintenance or repair should be considered.
- *Fire Safety Management.* Also, good housekeeping practices might be used as a method of controlling ignition, as well as the amount and type of combustibles that are present.

9.2.2 Control of Fire Development

9.2.2.1 Intent   The intent is to reduce the rate of development of a fire and the related smoke and heat production.

9.2.2.2 Concepts   Reduction of fire development is based on the following concepts:

- *Contents Selection.* The rate of fire growth might be controlled by selection and arrangement of the contents used in the building. Some contents have a high rate of heat release and that rate could also be dependent on their configuration[4] (i.e., sawdust versus a block of wood). Materials with a lesser propensity for ignition can help control fire growth and fire spread from object to object.
- *Placement of Contents.* The separation distance between objects is related to the ease for fire to spread from object to object.
- *Interior Finish Selection.* Similar to contents, combustible interior finishes can cause the fire to spread faster, particularly when placed on vertical surfaces or on the ceiling.
- *Compartment Geometry.* Large compartments with high ceilings tend to reduce the amount of radiant feedback to the fire and can, therefore, help decrease the rate of fire growth and spread.
- *Ventilation Control.* Fire development can be managed by controlling ventilation to the fire. However, when using ventilation control as a means of limiting fire growth, the effects on combustion gas temperatures, ignition of incomplete combustion gases remote from the fire, and carbon monoxide concentration should be considered.
- *Suppression Systems.* Suppression systems can be provided to limit the amount of heat being released by the fire and to limit the size to which it grows.
- *Construction.* The rate of fire growth could be affected by the construction features, materials, and design.

9.3 Spread Control and Management of Smoke

9.3.1 Intent

The intent is to reduce the hazard resulting from smoke by limiting its production, controlling its movement, or reducing its volume.

9.3.2 Concepts

Spread control and management of smoke are based on the following concepts:

- *Material Control.* Materials in the building and building construction can be controlled to limit or exclude those materials that produce large quantities of toxic smoke (i.e., plastics, etc.).

- *Containment.* Smoke can be contained to its area or compartment of origin by using such things as smoke control doors, smoke dampers, or lobbies.

- *Extraction.* Smoke can be removed from a compartment by natural or mechanical means. Large-volume spaces, such as atria, can be protected with smoke extraction systems to maintain tenable conditions in which occupants can egress and fire fighters can initiate firefighting efforts.

- *Pressurization.* Pressure differentials can be created to direct the movement of smoke from high-pressure areas to low-pressure areas. This technique is commonly used to prevent smoke from getting into lobbies and stairways and is sometimes implemented by pressurizing the floors above and below the fire floor and exhausting the fire floor, to keep smoke on the level of origin. By dividing a building into smoke zones and creating a pressure differential across those zones, smoke movement through cracks in floors and through shafts can be minimized. Zoned smoke control systems typically require a supplemental detection system that can control in which zones positive and negative pressures are created.

- *Suppression.* Application of a suppression system can reduce smoke development and limit smoke production and movement by limiting fire growth.

Note that when used in this guide, the term "smoke" includes the fire products of combustion and the air that is entrained (drawn in) into the fire plume. The primary constituent of smoke is the air that is entrained. When considering mass or volumetric smoke production rates, the mass flow of products of combustion (CO_2, H_2O, CO, etc.) are typically ignored because they constitute a very small portion of the smoke.[5] Their production rates are considered in the "species concentration" (see Section 9.3.3.1).

Several correlations are available[6,7 8] for flaming fires that yield smoke mass flow rate as a function of the height above the base of the fire. The design fire scenario forms the basis for the inputs for these correlations. Two of these references[5,7] could also be used to estimate the plume temperature as a function of height.

Detailed information on the design and evaluation of smoke management systems can be found in *Principles of Smoke Management,*[9] NFPA 92A[10] and NFPA 92B.[11]

Activation of a smoke management system typically occurs by either automatic detectors or manual means. The activation time can be determined in accordance with the detection and notification subsystem.

9.3.3 Additional Considerations Regarding Smoke

9.3.3.1 Species Concentration Estimation of species concentration in smoke requires information such as the ratio of air to fuel in the combustion zone. Tewarson provides a discussion on species generation in fires in *The SFPE Handbook of Fire Protection Engineering.*[12] In the absence of data on species production rates, a conservative approach might be to attempt to avoid exposure of occupants to smoke.

9.3.3.2 The Optical Density of Smoke   *The SFPE Handbook of Fire Protection Engineering* provides a table of maximum specific optical densities for a variety of commonly used materials.[13] The limitations of this data need to be understood, as it was developed with small-scale tests. The data might not be appropriate for complex fires. In the absence of other data, a conservative approach would be attempting to avoid exposure of occupants to smoke.

9.3.3.3 Upper Layer Temperature and Clear Layer Height   Calculation of the upper layer temperature and clear layer height is accomplished with calculations based[14] on empirical or theoretical equations.[15] These calculations can be performed by a computer fire model or by hand calculations.

9.3.3.4 Smoke Flow from Enclosures   The flow of smoke from enclosures can occur through openings such as doors, windows, or ventilation ducts. The calculation of smoke flow through these openings could be accomplished with certain fire models. Additionally, several calculation techniques are contained in *The SFPE Handbook of Fire Protection Engineering.*[16]

9.4 Fire Detection and Notification

9.4.1 Fire Detection

9.4.1.1 Intent   The intent is to provide warning of a fire in order to notify occupants or emergency personnel, or to activate an active fire protection system, such as a smoke management, door releases, or a suppression system.

9.4.1.2 Concepts   Fire detection is based on the following concepts:

- *Human detection.* Humans can detect fires. However, they must be in the vicinity and be alert and capable of sensing the various fire signatures and appropriately responding.
- *Automatic Detection.* Electro-mechanical detectors can be provided that monitor a space for various types of fire signatures (i.e., heat, smoke, radiant energy, etc.). Automatic detectors can be connected to an alarm system to alert building occupants as well as the fire department.

9.4.1.3 Delays

9.4.1.3 Delays   Most detection systems have inherent delays. These delays could be either variable or fixed.[17] Variable delays represent either transport lags associated with products of combustion reaching the detector or detector response delays. The delay associated with the transport of combustion products is a function of the heat release rate and smoke production rate of a fire, ceiling height, the radial distance of the detector from the fire, and obstructions. The delay associated with a heat detector response can be quantified if the detector's response time index (RTI) is known. For example, the computer model DETACT accounts for detector response delays by requiring RTI as input data.[18,19]

In many cases, a quasi-steady state is assumed, and the transport delays are ignored. However, the quasi-steady assumption might not be appropriate when long transport delays are expected, such as when high ceiling spaces exist or when very rapid detection is desired.

Fixed delays are associated with system characteristics, such as polling system delays, alarm verification time, or if a pre-alert is incorporated. System delays can be ascertained from manufacturer's data.

9.4.1.4 Estimation of Thermal Detector Response Time   Computer modeling is typically used to estimate thermal detector operation time. These models typically require the detector response characteristics, temperature rating, and enclosure geometry characteristics, such as ceiling height above the fire and detector radial distance from the fire centerline as input. *The SFPE Handbook of Fire Protection Engineering*[17] and Annex B of *NFPA 72* provides additional information on heat detector response, information on estimating smoke detector response time,[17] and an overall approach to design and analysis of detection systems.

9.4.2 Fire Notification

9.4.2.1 Intent   The intent is to notify the occupants of a building or the fire department that a fire has started and possibly provide information as to the location of the fire.

9.4.2.2 Concepts   Fire notification is based on the following concepts:

- Notification systems can be either human or electro-mechanical (i.e., automatic). If the notification system relies on humans, then the reliability of the system should be considered as part of the design.
- Audible and visual notification appliances can be initiated by a detection system to notify occupants in the area of fire origin that a fire has started.
- Notification messages should be both loud enough to be heard and understandable.

- If manual messages are to be broadcast, enough information should be provided to the person making the announcement so that appropriate direction is provided to the occupants.[20]

- Automatic detection system output can also be used to initiate notification to the fire department that a fire has started. Of interest here is whether the detection system output is sent to a central station or directly to the fire department. Criticality or importance of the protected facility sometimes dictates where the detection system output is sent.

- The process the fire department uses to receive and process a notification signal (i.e., alarm handling) can impact their response to the fire.

- Notification could also include the provision of information as to where the fire is (e.g., third floor electric closet) once the fire department is on the site. Notification of fire location can be performed by a detection system connected to an annunciator panel.

9.5 Fire Suppression

9.5.1 Intent The intent is to extinguish or control a fire.

9.5.2 Concepts The following are two types of fire suppression systems:

- *Automatic Suppression Systems.* Automatic suppression systems require no human interaction. These are either stand-alone systems or systems that require a detection system to active them. Suppression systems include sprinkler systems, gaseous suppression systems, and foam systems.

- *Manual Suppression Systems.* Manual fire fighting includes fire fighting actions taken by occupants, fire brigades, or fire departments. First aid firefighting appliances (i.e., those intended for use by building occupants) including fire extinguishers, hose reels, and sand buckets can be used to begin fire suppression activities. However, unless the fire is small, these efforts are not necessarily expected to extinguish a fire. Therefore, additional suppression could be needed. This additional suppression might be provided by automatic suppression systems or by organized manual suppression systems, such as fire departments and fire brigades.

Suppression systems can be used to meet life safety and/or property protection objectives. Additionally, suppression systems can be used as a means of fire detection (e.g., a water flow switch on a sprinkler system).

9.5.3 Automatic Fire Suppression Systems

9.5.3.1 Impact of Automatic Fire Suppression   Where automatic fire suppression systems are installed, and assuming they are activated when they are designed to do so, then the design fire curve might be modified, as shown in Figure 9-4.

The time at which the suppression system activates is dependent upon the system design and the mechanism used to activate it. Section 10.4.2.2 identifies a procedure for estimating the activation time of suppression systems.

An important concept is that of control versus extinguishment (complete suppression). Traditional sprinkler systems might only control fires, i.e., prevent the heat release rate from increasing further. On the other hand, gaseous systems and some forms of sprinkler systems might extinguish the fire. The impact of a suppression system is illustrated in Figure 9-4.

9.5.3.2 Delays   As with detection systems, suppression systems can have delays that are associated with system operation; these delays should be evaluated. In addition to the delays described in Section 9.4.1.3, additional delays can include delays associated with agent discharge, reaching an extinguishing concentration, and predischarge warning delays.

For wet pipe sprinkler systems, the discharge delay can typically be ignored. However, for dry pipe or deluge systems, the discharge delay needs to be evaluated. *The SFPE Handbook of Fire Protection Engineering* provides a formula for estimating the operation time for a dry pipe valve.[21] Computer software is also available[22,23] to calculate dry pipe water delivery times. Software is also available[24] to estimate the discharge time for gaseous suppression systems.

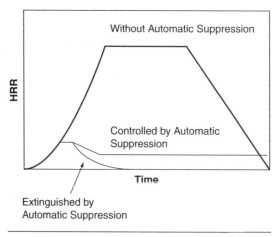

FIGURE 9-4   Impact of Automatic Fire Suppression Systems

9.5.4 Manual Fire Fighting Operations

9.5.4.1 Concepts   Manual fire fighting operations are based on the following concepts:

- *Notification.* The emergency response forces require notification of a fire. Notification should include as much information as possible as to the location of the building as well as the location of the fire within the building.
- *Access.* The emergency response forces and their equipment should have easy access both to the site of the building and to the area of fire origin. The existence of gates and fences, as well as secured buildings, will delay the fire department's response to the area of origin. Access can also include protected stairways and corridors so that fire department personnel can get as close to the origin as possible.
- *Water supply.* The fire department should be provided with an adequate water supply on site (e.g., fire hydrants or cisterns) as well as within the building (e.g., standpipes or hose reels).
- *Smoke clearance.* Provisions might need to be made to clear smoke and heat during firefighting operations as well as after firefighting operations to facilitate firefighting and rescue operations.

9.5.4.2 Other Considerations

9.5.4.2.1 Capability and Capacity   When considering the effect of fire department and emergency response force operations in a performance-based design, careful consideration should be given to the abilities of the local fire department.[25] These abilities can be divided into two categories: capability and capacity.

9.5.4.2.2 Capability   A fire department's capability is a measure of the department's ability to respond within a short time with a sufficient number of trained personnel and equipment adequate to meet a set of objectives.

9.5.4.2.3 Capacity   Capacity is a measure of the ability of a department to respond adequately to multiple alarm incidents or simultaneous calls.

9.5.4.2.4 Delays   There can be significant delays associated with fire department response that should be considered when fire department operations are part of a performance-based design. These delays can come from several sources,[26] and include the following:

- Detection delay is the delay associated with detecting a fire and initiating a response by the fire department.
- Dispatch delay is the delay associated with receiving and processing an emergency call. The transition between detection delay and dispatch

delay occurs when the fire department or emergency response force has direct, contractual control, or approval authority of the equipment (e.g., a telephone switching system or central station facility).

- Turnout delay is the time it takes the responding emergency response personnel to react and prepare to leave the station. Turnout time stops when the wheels on the apparatus start to turn.
- Travel time is the time that elapses from when the apparatus starts to move forward until the apparatus reaches the incident scene.
- Access time is the time required for the department to move from the apparatus to the emergency location.
- Setup time is the time required to prepare to commence operations. The level of effort (e.g., first responders and reinforcements) must be defined as part of the setup time. It is possible to have multiple setup times if fire response is staged.
- Suppression time is the time required to suppress a fire.
- Delays associated with apparatus already in service and awaiting call-back for manpower is also a consideration depending on staffing of the fire department.

9.5.4.2.5 Impact of Fire Department Suppression Operations   Fire departments can limit further fire spread by using two basic suppression tactics: extinguishment and containment. Extinguishment is commonly accomplished by direct application of water into the fire compartment. Figure 9-5 demonstrates a possible heat release rate (HRR) over time for such an extinguishment tactic. Containment is accomplished by preventing fire extension to uninvolved portions of the building. Water is typically applied to surrounding walls and exposures, whereas the involved contents are allowed to burn to completion.

Fire departments might not reach a building and start suppression operations until after flashover. In addition, suppression could be delayed because

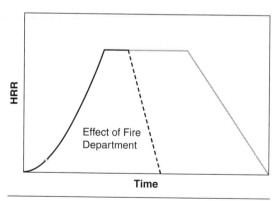

FIGURE 9-5   Possible Effect of Fire Department Operations

of higher priorities, such as rescue. In some instances, suppression might not be the desired tactic. If the building is considered sacrificial, and the contents of very high value (e.g., artwork), one emergency response alternative may be removal of the contents rather than direct fire suppression. If this is the design approach, it should be documented in the performance-based design (PBD) report to ensure that all the stakeholders are in agreement.

9.6 Occupant Behavior and Egress

9.6.1 Intent

The intent is to allow the occupants to travel without harm to a place of safety in the event of a fire.

9.6.2 Concepts

Occupant behavior and egress involves the following concepts:

- *Access.* Occupants should be able to access an exit.
- *Protected escape route.* Exits might need to be fire rated to limit the potential for smoke and heat inflow until the last occupant can reach a place of safety.
- *Protect in place.* Protection can be provided such that occupants are safe inside the building.

9.6.3 Occupant Preparation

Occupants should be provided with detection and notification of a fire event. Occupants should also be provided with sufficient means to leave the building or area, including access to a sufficient number of exits, sufficient exit capacity, emergency lighting, directional signs, and a protected route to an area of safety. For more information on occupant behavior, see Section 8.5.3.

9.7 Passive Fire Protection

9.7.1 Providing Structural Stability

9.7.1.1 Intent   The intent is to prevent the premature collapse of part or all of a structure.

9.7.1.2 Concepts   The following are two ways in which the structural stability of a building can be increased:

- *Inherent Stability.* Structural elements can be designed so that they can withstand exposure to the expected fire severity without prematurely collapsing. The design of the structural elements should take into account the loading of the structural element, the amount and duration of exposure to fire, and the effects of deformation

- *Supplemental Protection.* If the inherent features of a structural element are not sufficient to maintain its strength, then protection can be applied directly to the structural element or a barrier can be provided between the fire and the element to reduce the heat transfer to the structure.

Methods are available to determine the protection necessary for structural members to avoid structural collapse due to the thermal impact associated with exposure to elevated temperatures.[27,28,29] These calculation methods can consider either a standardized time-temperature relationship or a design fire scenario (see Chapter 8, "Developing Trial Designs").

9.7.1.3 Other Considerations

9.7.1.3.1 Structural Fire Resistance Ratings   Building and fire safety regulations require varying structural fire resistance ratings that are dependent on the characteristics of the building and its occupancy classification. These fire resistance ratings are based on a structural element's response to a standardized fire test procedure.[30] It should be understood that these standardized fire test procedures might not represent actual fire conditions, and therefore fire performance during an actual fire might not be as expected. Additionally, these standardized fire test procedures might not address complicated or unusual structural connections where load redistribution might occur. Consideration should be given to a detailed fire and structural response analysis to provide a more accurate assessment of a structure's integrity during a fire.

9.7.1.3.2 Response to Fire of Structural Elements   Heat affects the load-bearing capacity of structural elements, whether structural elements are constructed of steel, concrete, or wood. It is therefore important to understand the thermal and mechanical response of the various structural elements and their performance and ability to support their load and limit deformations and elongations. Various factors should therefore be part of the assessment.[30] These include loading of the structural elements, composite action of floor slabs/frames, potential transfer of loads, susceptibility to progressive collapse, and stability and performance of connections. There are numerous papers, research and models[31] available to assist with the analysis.[27]

When assessing the structure's response to fire, there are several factors that should be part of the analysis.[30] These include the following: the fire exposure, the transfer of heat to the structural elements, and the response of the structure to the changes in temperature.[32] Heat transfer into the structure may be affected by the presence, type, and quantity of fireproofing. Due to their thermal mass, large structural elements may have an inherent resistance to rapidly reaching elevated temperatures. They may also be designed to withstand fires of varying severity and duration, for instance by increasing their size, redundancy, and location relative to fuel load.

9.7.1.3.3 Threats of Impacts and Explosions There may be other types of threats, such as blasts, impacts, and explosions, that may be deemed to be design events and that may impact the fire performance of the structure.[30] If so, it is important to assess the resiliency of the fireproofing and also the damage that could be caused by an impact or explosion. Understanding the ability of the structure to redistribute and carry load under fire conditions without disproportionate collapse may also be an important factor that should be taken into consideration.

9.7.2 Limiting Fire Spread through Passive Means

9.7.2.1 Intent The intent is to prevent a fire from spreading from the room of fire origin to other areas or compartments of the building.

9.7.2.2 Concepts The following are passive means of limiting fire spread:

- *Compartmentation.* Buildings can be divided by fire barriers to isolate compartments that are not the room of fire origin from the effects of heat and smoke.
- *Fire Barriers.* Fire barriers provide horizontal and vertical barriers to fire and smoke, typically provided in compartment boundaries. They are designed to resist the penetration of heat and smoke for a given amount of time.
- *Protection of Openings.* Openings in barriers provide a ready avenue for fire spread. Fire spread through openings can be controlled by the following techniques:
  - Fire-stopping openings where piping, wiring, conduit, or other items penetrate barriers.
  - Ensuring doors are closed in the event of a fire. This can be accomplished by the use of automatic closing mechanisms or educating occupants to close doors in the event of a fire.
  - Use of fire resistant glazing materials. Ordinary glass has relatively little fire integrity.[33] Therefore, additional preventive measures should be taken when glass is used in a barrier.
- *External Spread.* Consideration should be given to a building's interior and external fire spread potential when a fire could breach the building envelope and attack upper floors.
- *Controlling the Fire.* Automatic suppression systems can be used to assist in the containment of fire by reducing the severity of the fire.

Notes

1. NFPA 550, *Guide to the Fire Safety Concepts Tree*, 2002 edition, National Fire Protection Association, Quincy, MA.

2. *Engineering Guide: Piloted Ignition of Solid Materials Under Radiant Exposure*, Society of Fire Protection Engineers, Bethesda, MD, 2002.

3. Rockett, J.A., & Milke, J.A. "Conduction of Heat in Solids," *The SFPE Handbook of Fire Protection Engineering*, 3rd Edition, National Fire Protection Association, Quincy, MA, 2002.

4. Bukowski, R. "Fire Hazard Analysis," *Fire Protection Handbook*, 19th Edition, National Fire Protection Association, 2003.

5. Heskestad, G. "Fire Plumes, Flame Height, and Air Entrainment," *The SFPE Handbook of Fire Protection Engineering*, 3rd Edition, National Fire Protection Association, Quincy, MA, 2002.

6. Zukoski, Kubota, & Cetegen. "Entrainment in Fire Plumes," *Fire Safety Journal*, Vol. 3, pp. 107–121, 1980.

7. McCaffrey, B. "Purely Buoyant Diffusion Flames: Some Experimental Results," National Institute of Standards and Technology, NBSIR 79-1910, 1979.

8. Thomas, P., Hinkley, P., Theobald, C., & Simms, D. "Investigations into the flow of hot gasses in roof venting," Fire Research Technical Paper No. 7, HMSO, London, 1963.

9. Klote, J.H., & Milke, J.A. *Principles of Smoke Management*, American Society of Heating, Refrigerating and Air-Conditioning Engineers, 2002.

10. NFPA 92A, *Standard for Smoke-Control Systems Utilizing Barriers and Pressure Differences*, 2006 edition, National Fire Protection Association, Quincy, MA.

11. NFPA 92B, *Standard for Smoke Management Systems in Malls, Atria and Large Areas*, 2005 edition, National Fire Protection Association, Quincy, MA.

12. Tewarson, A. "Generation of Heat and Chemical Compounds in Fires," *The SFPE Handbook of Fire Protection Engineering*, 3rd Edition, National Fire Protection Association, Quincy, MA, 2002.

13. Mulholland, G. "Smoke Production and Properties," *The SFPE Handbook of Fire Protection Engineering*, 3rd Edition, National Fire Protection Association, Quincy, MA, 2002.

14. Walton, D. "ASET-B: A Room Fire Program for Personal Computers," NBSIR 85-3144-1, National Bureau of Standards, 1985.

15. Cooper, L. "Smoke and Heat Venting," *The SFPE Handbook of Fire Protection Engineering*, 3rd Edition, National Fire Protection Association, Quincy, MA, 2002.

16. Emmons, H. "Vent Flows," *The SFPE Handbook of Fire Protection Engineering*, 3rd Edition, National Fire Protection Association, Quincy, MA, 2002.

17. Schifiliti, R., Meacham, B., & Custer, R. "Design of Detection Systems," *The SFPE Handbook of Fire Protection Engineering*, National Fire Protection Association, 3rd Edition, Quincy, MA, 2002.

18. Evans, D., & Stroup, D. "Methods to Calculate the Response Time of Heat and Smoke Detectors Installed Below Large Unobstructed Ceilings," NBSIR 85-3167, National Bureau of Standards, Gaithersburg, MD, 1985.

19. *Engineering Guide—Evaluation of the Computer Fire Model DETACT-QS*, Society of Fire Protection Engineers, Bethesda, MD, 2002.

20. *Engineering Guide—Human Behavior in Fire*, Society of Fire Protection Engineers, Bethesda, MD, 2003.

21. Fleming, R. "Automatic Sprinkler System Calculations," *The SFPE Handbook of Fire Protection Engineering*, 3rd Edition, National Fire Protection Association, Quincy, MA, 2002.

22. Golinveaux, J. "Dry-Pipe Sprinkler Software," *NFPA Journal*, Mar/Apr 2004.

23. Dubay, C., ed. *Automatic Sprinkler Systems Handbook*, National Fire Protection Association, Quincy, MA, 2002.

24. AgentCalcs, Hughes Associates, Inc., Baltimore, MD.

25. Paulsgrove, R. "Fire Department Administration and Operations," *Fire Protection Handbook*, 19th Edition, National Fire Protection Association, Quincy, MA, 2003.

26. Barr, R.C., & Caputo, A.P. "Planning Fire Station Locations," *Fire Protection Handbook*, 19th Edition, National Fire Protection Association, Quincy, MA, 2003.

27. Milke, J. "Analytical Methods for Determining Fire Resistance of Steel Members," *The SFPE Handbook of Fire Protection Engineering*, 3rd Edition, National Fire Protection Association, Quincy, MA, 2002.

28. Fleishmann, C., & Buchanan, A. "Analytical Methods for Determining Fire Resistance of Concrete Members," *The SFPE Handbook of Fire Protection Engineering*, 3rd Edition, National Fire Protection Association, Quincy, MA, 2002.

29. White, R. "Analytical Methods for Determining Fire Resistance of Timber Members," *The SFPE Handbook of Fire Protection Engineering*, 3rd Edition, National Fire Protection Association, Quincy, MA, 2002.

30. Marrion, C. "Design of Structures for Fire Loading and Understanding Fire/Life Safety System Interdependencies," ASCE Structures Congress, New York, 2005.

31. ASCE/SEI/SFPE 29-99, *Standard Calculation Methods for Structural Fire Protection*, American Society of Civil Engineers and Society of Fire Protection Engineers, 2003.

32. *Engineering Guide—Fire Exposures to Structural Elements*, Society of Fire Protection Engineers, Bethesda, MD, 2004.

33. Gore Willse, P.J. "Structural Integrity During Fire," *Fire Protection Handbook*, 19th Edition, National Fire Protection Association, Quincy, MA, 2003.

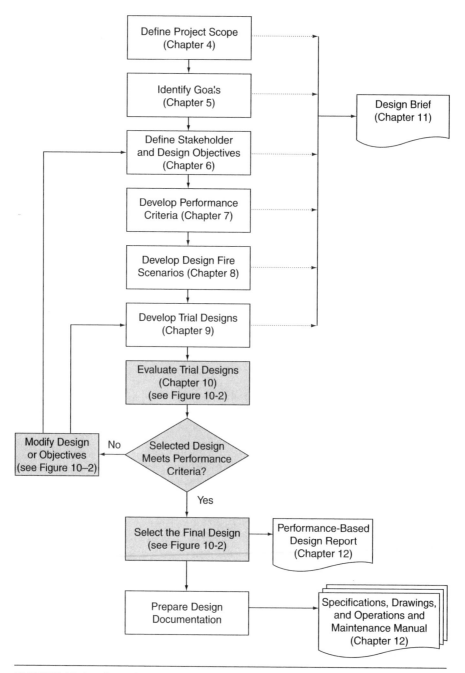

FIGURE 10-1 Overview of the Performance-Based Design Process, Evaluating Trial Designs

CHAPTER 10

Evaluating Trial Designs

10.1 General

Evaluation is the process of determining if a trial design meets the performance criteria when challenged by the design fire scenarios. For more information on developing trial designs and developing performance criteria, see Chapters 9 and 7, respectively. Figure 10-1 shows the overall performance-based design process and the position of Chapter 10 within that process.

10.1.1 Evaluation of Trial Designs A selected series of trial design(s) are evaluated against each design fire scenario. The intent is to demonstrate that the performance criteria will not be exceeded. If a particular trial design is successful, any remaining trial designs would be evaluated as necessary to demonstrate that the overall building design will meet the performance criteria for the design fire scenarios. If a trial design is not successful, the trial design should be modified and retested, or it could be dismissed and replaced with an entirely new trial design. After the selected trial designs have been tested, a specific trial design, or series of trial designs, would be selected to represent the overall building design specification.

If there are no successful trial designs, the engineer should ensure that the trial designs took all possible mitigation strategies into consideration. If after considering the trial designs, none are successful, the stakeholder objectives and performance criteria could be revisited, as shown in Figure 10-2.

10.1.1.1 It is recommended that the engineer adopt a systematic approach to conducting the evaluation. Established analytical techniques should be used to evaluate the response of the trial design for each scenario. The predicted outcome (e.g., loss, consequence, or results) must then be compared to the performance criteria. If the outcome is favorable when compared to the

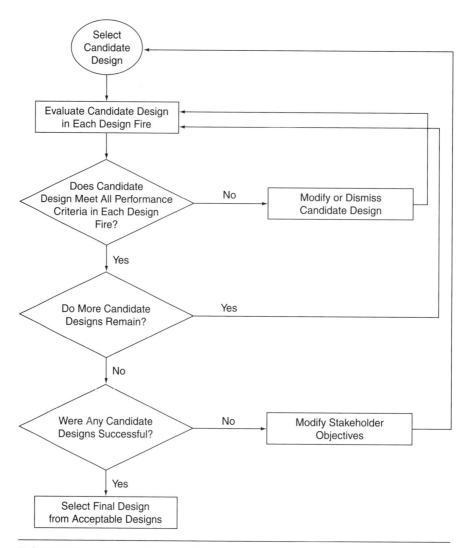

FIGURE 10-2 Evaluating Trial Designs

performance criteria, then the design is successful for the evaluated design fire scenario. For a design to be considered acceptable, it must be successful for all of the established design scenarios.

10.1.1.2 The evaluation process can be described in a three-step process. The first step establishes the purpose and type of evaluation. In other words, step one identifies what the analysis is supposed to accomplish, and if the analysis will be probabilistic or deterministic. Step one is referred to as "the evaluation level" as discussed in Section 10.2. The second step is to conduct the evaluation, as described in Section 10.3 for probabilistic analyses and

Section 10.4 for deterministic analyses. The third and final step is to account for variations and uncertainties in the evaluation process that can impact the outcome as described in Section 10.5.

10.1.1.3 There are several different techniques that can be used to account for known variations and uncertainties in the evaluation process. Safety factors can provide a simple approach in this regard. If safety factors have not been quantified, there are several other methods that can be used. These are discussed in Sections 10.5.4 and 10.5.5. In addition, it is usually appropriate to establish the robustness of the analysis. Techniques to accomplish this are discussed in Section 10.5.6.

10.1.2 Level of Analysis
The technical detail needed varies with the evaluation level (see Section 10.2). System- or building-level applications could require independent evaluations of the individual fire protection components as well as a higher-order evaluation of the complete building design. Prior to beginning the evaluation process, the level of evaluation necessary should be established and agreed to by the stakeholders.

10.1.3 Developing a Plan
Before any evaluation is initiated, a plan should be established that allows the design team to understand the analysis level that will be used, and also the analytical models (simplifications, assumptions, etc.) and analytical tools to be understood. It is important that individual pieces be coordinated and the assumptions be consistent.

10.1.4 Selecting Evaluation Tools
The tools (models, computer software, etc.) that are selected to perform the evaluation must be valid and applicable to the problem. Models and computer software must be demonstrated to be valid. ASTM E-1355, *Standard Guide for Evaluating the Predictive Capability of Deterministic Fire Models*,[1] provides one validation approach that can be used. If the model or computer software has not been demonstrated as valid in a peer-reviewed process, the engineer must demonstrate the validity of the model or computer software to the satisfaction of the authority having jurisdiction.

10.1.5 Effectiveness, Reliability, Availability, and Cost
When considering whether a trial design meets specific performance criteria, factors such as effectiveness, reliability, availability, and cost should be considered.

10.1.5.1 The *effectiveness* of a trial design is judged by determining whether the design meets the established performance criteria. The combination of system reliability and availability is the system's effectiveness.

10.1.5.2 *Reliability* measures whether a design or system will function as designed or intended. For example, a sprinkler system has functioned as designed if the system discharges sufficient water to control or extinguish a fire without excessive fire spread.

10.1.5.3 A design or system is considered *available* whenever it is capable of performing a required function at a given instant in time. Thus, the system could be unavailable during testing, unplanned maintenance, preventive maintenance, and planned modifications. A common failure for many fire protection systems is failure to restore to service following maintenance. Based on this definition of available, a system left inoperative following maintenance is considered unavailable. If this impaired system were required to operate and did not fulfill its design function, it would be an availability failure.

10.1.5.4 System *costs* can be used to help evaluate the feasibility of trial designs. Costs that should be considered include initial installation costs, costs associated with inspection and maintenance, and costs associated with maximum acceptable fire damage. If the cost of a trial design is more than the client is willing to pay, consideration of the trial design might not be warranted. However, if no trial designs fall within the client's budget, the stakeholder's goals and objectives should be reevaluated. Also, if several successful trial designs are available, cost could be one of the factors used to select which successful alternative is used.

10.1.6 Time Line for Key Events

Time lines can be valuable tools for evaluating trial designs. Therefore, determination of the time of the following key events could be necessary:

- Ignition
- Fire detection
- Evacuation start and finish
- Untenable conditions reached in room of origin
- Window failure
- Flashover
- Fire spread beyond room of origin
- Manual suppression
- Failure of structural elements
- Fire extinguishment

The key events will likely be related to the trial design option being evaluated and should be selected accordingly.

10.1.6.1 The heat release rate associated with a design fire scenario can serve as a key input into the calculation methods for determining the time of many of these events. In other applications, the heat release rate is calculated as part of the calculation method (e.g., computer model).[2]

10.1.6.2 For some events, the activation of certain systems leads to a modification of the design fire curve that would otherwise eventuate. For example, if a growing fire activates sprinklers, the heat release rate of the fire will be limited or reduced.

10.1.7 Evaluation Techniques

Various techniques can be used to evaluate the adequacy of a trial design, and they typically range from, deterministic methods to probabilistic approaches. A *deterministic method* examines a specific design fire scenario to determine the potential outcome as described in Section 10.4. A *probabilistic approach* considers the likelihood of a certain event occurring, such as a specific design fire scenario. Probabilistic approaches can include a risk-informed evaluation, such as outlined in the *SFPE Engineering Guide to Fire Risk Assessment*.[3] Two probabilistic methods are presented in this guide—the classical (explicit) risk analysis method and a risk binning analysis, as described in Sections 10.3.1 and 10.3.2, respectively. When completing an evaluation, there is an implicit assumption that an outcome more severe than that proposed is not credible or is not within the scope of the performance-based design (PBD) project.

10.2 Levels of Evaluation

10.2.1 Factors Affecting Evaluation

The performance-based design process can be used to evaluate and recommend fire protection options at the subsystem-performance level, at the system-performance level, or at the building-performance level. Evaluations at each of these levels could be performed as comparative analyses or analyses and designs to defined performance criteria. The evaluation level necessary for a performance-based design project is a function of several factors. These factors include the following:

- Complexity of geometry
- Level of subsystem interaction
- Type of performance/acceptance criteria

- Sensitivity of subsystem output to design objectives
- Absolute or comparative evaluation
- Knowledge level (uncertainties)
- Benefit versus cost
- Expert judgment and experience

10.2.2 Subsystem Performance

10.2.2.1 A subsystem-performance evaluation typically consists of a simple comparative analysis and could be used to demonstrate that a selected component or subsystem provides equivalent performance to that specified by a prescriptive-based code. At this level, one subsystem is evaluated in isolation.

10.2.2.2 A comparative analysis typically uses analytical calculations to demonstrate equivalent performance of the proposed alternative component or system. Although these analyses could be deterministic or probabilistic, deterministic methods would normally be used. A deterministic subsystem-performance evaluation could involve applying the same models, calculations, input data, and acceptance criteria for the trial design(s) and the code-mandated solution to which equivalence is sought.

For example, a subsystem-performance evaluation could be appropriate when considering an alternative fire detection system to that specified in a prescriptive-based code. Trial fire detection system designs could involve different types of detection devices, different spacing of detectors, or other changes to individual components or parts of the system. A trial design that resulted in detector activation and alarm signaling at a time or fire size that is equal to or earlier than the code-prescribed solution could be considered acceptable.

Similarly, a particular fire-rated structural element could be prescribed in a prescriptive-based code. A different structural element or a different approach to providing an equivalent level of fire resistance for a structural element could be considered acceptable in a performance-based analysis and design if the trial design can provide equivalent structural performance through a subsystem-performance evaluation.

10.2.2.3 In both of the previous examples, the evaluation was performed, and the results were compared to a prescriptive-based code. Evaluation of the detection system or the fire resistance in terms of the goals and objectives of the stakeholders rather than a prescriptive-based code is also possible. For a detection system, the objective could be to alert people in time for them safely to leave the building. For fire resistance, the objective could be for the fire to be contained to the compartment of origin and for the structure to remain in place through a complete compartment burnout.

10.2.3 System-Performance Evaluations

10.2.3.1 A system-performance evaluation could consist of a comparative analysis or an analysis and design to performance criteria developed from goals and objectives of the stakeholders. A system-performance evaluation is used when an entire or a substantial part of a building design is being considered (e.g., the exit system) and more than one fire protection system or feature is involved (e.g., fire resistance ratings and suppression systems).

10.2.3.2 A system-performance evaluation is more complex than a subsystem-performance evaluation because the analysis needs to take account of the interaction between various systems and components. A system-performance analysis will often be based on one or more worst case scenarios (see Chapter 8, "Developing Design Fire Scenarios").

10.2.3.3 In a system-performance comparative analysis, identical design fire scenarios should be used, and identical data, input parameters, and models must be used in both analyses. If this is done, any assumptions regarding rate of fire growth, choice of fire model, occupant characteristics, material response, or the like might not have a significant influence on the outcome. The analysis could be deterministic or risk based.

10.2.3.4 A system-performance evaluation could be appropriate for alternative design proposals that are not radically different from those included in prescriptive-based codes.

For example, a system-performance evaluation could be appropriate when a designer is proposing an atrium smoke management system with different performance criteria than specified in a code. In this situation, the engineer must analyze various fire and life safety issues, such as fire growth rates, smoke development, times for detection and suppression, smoke control system performance, and occupant egress. This analysis involves a number of fire protection systems and therefore requires a system-performance evaluation.

10.2.4 Building-Performance Evaluations

10.2.4.1 A building-performance evaluation is appropriate for complex or unique buildings in which substantial analysis could lead to a clear understanding of the hazards and risks, to the resolution of complex design problems, and to the potential for significant cost savings. This building-performance analysis considers how the fire protection system interacts with the rest of the building. (An example could be using the potable water supply for the sprinkler system.)

10.2.4.2   By assigning probabilities of failure to the fire protection measures and assigning frequencies of occurrence to unwanted events, a probabilistic analysis can combine a number of different design fire scenarios as part of a complete fire safety assessment.

10.3 Probabilistic Analysis

10.3.1 Classical Risk Analysis

If the effect of probabilities and reliabilities is to be explicitly considered, a risk-based method must be used. A classical risk analysis is one technique that can accomplish this. This analysis requires a high degree of capability on the part of the engineers performing and reviewing the analysis. Also, because of the significant amount of statistical data and quantitative analysis, careful attention must be given to uncertainty.

10.3.1.1 Overview   In a classical risk analysis, the frequency of each design fire scenario and the reliability of each component of the fire protection system must be quantified. Possible sources of reliability and availability data include historical data for similar facilities, systems, or components (see Appendix E for methods to quantify risk).

10.3.1.2 Procedure   The steps required to complete a classical risk analysis are as follows:

1. Develop design fire scenarios, and determine associated frequencies of occurrence.
2. Determine the reliability of the trial design.
3. Quantify the loss associated with the design fire scenario, assuming that the trial design is successful (see Section 10.3.1.3 for further discussion).
4. Quantify the loss associated with the design fire scenario, assuming that the trial design fails (see Section 10.3.1.3 for further discussion).
5. Repeat for each design fire scenario.
6. Calculate the total risk associated with the trial design.
7. Repeat for each trial design.

10.3.1.3 Success and Failure Modes For some trial designs, there could be intermediate levels of success or failure. These intermediate modes can be an important strategy for fire risk reduction. Different failure modes for a single subsystem, such as the suppression subsystem described in Chapter 9, will result in different levels of loss. If the main valve of a sprinkler is improperly closed, the potential loss could be the entire building. If a sectional valve is improperly closed, the potential loss could be the associated section of the building. If a single sprinkler fails to actuate, a single room could be lost. When stated in terms of success, the outcomes could be as follows:

- A single sprinkler operation limits the damage to a small area.
- A multiple sprinkler operation limits the damage to the room of origin.
- An extensive number of sprinklers activate and limit the fire to a single floor.
- An extensive number of sprinklers activate and do not control the fire, but they do provide early notification and delay fire spread until evacuation is complete. The number of outcomes that must be considered depends on the project details and the required analysis accuracy.

10.3.2 Risk Binning Analysis

10.3.2.1 Overview As an alternative to a classical risk analysis, the risk binning[4] technique is simpler to apply. The importance of identifying all possible outcomes is less critical. By quantifying the consequences of the most severe events and coupling these with approximate event frequencies, an approximate, quantified risk estimate is possible.

10.3.2.2 Consequence Ranking The following guidelines can be used when working with consequence rankings:

1. A maximum consequence for each type of loss (e.g., occupant loss, monetary loss, business interruption, or environmental damage) should be identified. The consequences should represent the largest realistic event of each type.

2. Each maximum consequence must be ranked. Table 10-1 provides an example of possible consequence-ranking thresholds (e.g., negligible, low, moderate, and high). The consequence predictions at this stage should bound (95 percent or better coverage) all possible event outcomes.

3. The 95 percent coverage value is suggested because it has gained ready acceptance in other engineering fields.[5,6] By using this standard value, a comparison of different analyses is possible. If the use of an alternate coverage value is desired, all stakeholders should agree with this variation.

TABLE 10-1   Possible Consequence Ranking Criteria

Consequence Level	Impact on Populace	Impact on Property/Operations
High (H)	Prompt fatalities, acute injuries—immediately life threatening or permanently disabling	Damage > $XX million Building destroyed and surrounding property damaged
Moderate (M)	Serious injuries, permanent disabilities, hospitalization required	$YY < damage < $XX million Major equipment destroyed Minor impact on surroundings
Low (L)	Minor injuries, no permanent disabilities, no hospitalization	Damage < $YY Reparable damage to building, significant operational down-time, no impact on surroundings
Negligible (N)	Negligible injuries	Minor repairs to building required Minimal operational down-time

4. When selecting the maximum consequence, an extensive analysis can often be avoided if the total replacement costs are assumed to be the maximum consequence.

10.3.2.3 Frequency Ranking   The following guidelines can be used when working with frequency rankings:

1. The frequencies must also be ranked. Table 10-2 gives a sample description for frequency ranking.[4]

2. The frequencies should be for exceeding a specific loss (i.e., consequence) rather than for exceeding a specific scenario. Frequencies based solely on a specific scenario can be misleading. (A scenario could have a frequency of 1×10^{-7} per year. The conclusion could be that *fire is not a concern*. However, the reported fire risk should represent the frequency of multiple fire scenarios. If 30 specific scenarios are developed, each at 1×10^{-7} fires per year, the net effect is 3×10^{-6} fires per year.)

3. Alternate frequency rankings (bins) from those presented in Table 10-2 can be developed. Like the consequence rankings, all stakeholders should

TABLE 10-2 Example Frequency Criteria Used for Probability Ranking

Acronym	Description	Frequency level (Median time to event)	Description
A	Anticipated, expected	> 1E-2/yr (<100 years)	Incidents that could occur several times during the lifetime of the building. (Incidents that commonly occur.)
U	Unlikely	1E-4 < f < 1E-2/yr (100 to 10,000 years)	Events that are not anticipated to occur during the lifetime of the facility. Natural phenomena of this probability class include: UBC-level earthquake, 100-year flood, maximum wind gust, etc.
EU	Extremely unlikely	1E-6 < f < 1E-4/yr (10,000 to 1 million years)	Events that will probably not occur during the life cycle of the building
BEU	Beyond extremely unlikely	< 1E-6/yr (> 1 million years)	All other accidents

agree to the alternate values. It is even reasonable to add additional layers of ranking (e.g., single order of magnitude width rather than double orders of magnitude width).

10.3.2.4 Risk Ranking   The following guidelines can be used when working with risk rankings:

1. Once the bounding consequences and their respective frequencies have been estimated, they must be converted to a risk, which is accomplished by plotting the consequence–frequency combination on the matrix as shown in Figure 10-3. (The numbers in the boxes are for identification and do not imply a ranking.) Each consequence–frequency combination is assigned a relative risk level by the stakeholders. These resultant risks are considered bounding risks.

Frequency→ Consequence↓	Beyond Extremely Unlikely $f \leq 10^{-6}\,yr^{-1}$	Extremely Unlikely $10^{-4} \geq f > 10^{-6}\,yr^{-1}$	Unlikely $10^{-2} \geq f > 10^{-4}\,yr^{-1}$	Anticipated $f > 10^{-2}\,yr^{-1}$
High		7	4	1
Moderate	10	8	5	2
Low		9	6	3
Negligible	11	12		

Key

■ High risk   ▨ Moderate risk   ☐ Low risk   ☐ Negligible risk

FIGURE 10-3   Example Risk Ranking Matrix

2. After this analysis, events that meet certain risk criteria may be considered acceptable, depending on the stakeholders' objectives. For example, the stakeholders could consider moderate, low, and negligible risk events acceptable.

10.4 Deterministic Analysis

10.4.1 Prerequisites

10.4.1.1   In a deterministic analysis, the expected performance of the fire protection system is analyzed against one or more design fire scenarios. When multiple design fire scenarios have been developed, they should be considered independently.

10.4.1.2   Time lines can be useful in a deterministic analysis. Descriptive factors of the design fire scenario (e.g., ignition, growth, and critical heat release rates) can be plotted on the time line along with the times of occurrence of key events of the fire protection system.

10.4.1.3 For the trial design to be successful, each performance criterion must be met in each of the design fires with consideration given to uncertainties due to known variations and unknown effects. Factors that could introduce uncertainty into the analysis include material variations, installation unknowns, system and component variability, unanticipated use of systems, and unpredictable future human actions.

10.4.2 Analytical Models

Fire models or other types of analytical analysis are often used as the basis for deterministic analysis. Appendix F provides information on the selection of models or other analytical methods. The analytical methods used should be capable of determining if the performance criteria will be achieved in the design fire scenarios. The following diagrams identify possible analysis procedures for determining if different types of performance criteria have been met. Supplement 7 of the *Life Safety Code® Handbook*[7] provides examples of deterministic analyses.

10.4.2.1 Prevention of Fire Spread Figure 10-4 provides a possible methodology for considering fire spread from enclosures.

10.4.2.2 Fire Detection Figure 10-5 provides an overview of the process of estimating the detector activation time for a given design fire scenario. When using this methodology, it should be noted that in some cases a design fire scenario might not activate a detector. The methodology presented in Figure 10-5 is essentially the same process as the computer model DETACT[8] uses.

10.4.2.3 Occupant Evacuation Figure 10-6 provides an overview of the process for estimating evacuation time.

10.4.2.4 Smoke Control Figure 10-7 provides an overview of the process for evaluating a smoke control system.

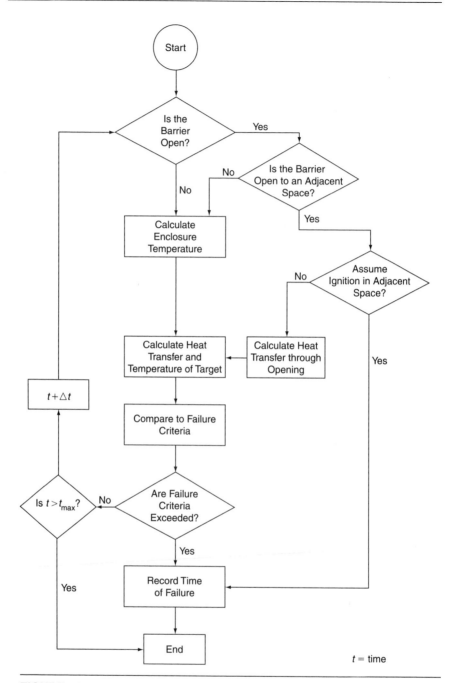

FIGURE 10-4   Methodology for Considering Fire Spread from Enclosures

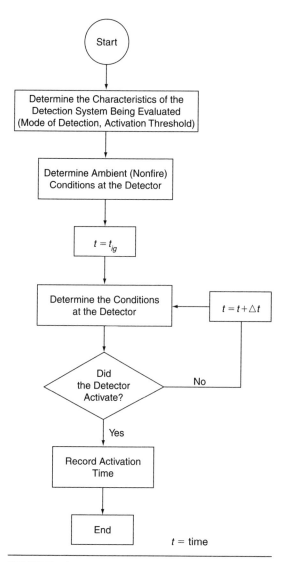

FIGURE 10-5 Methodology for Estimating the Detector Activation Time

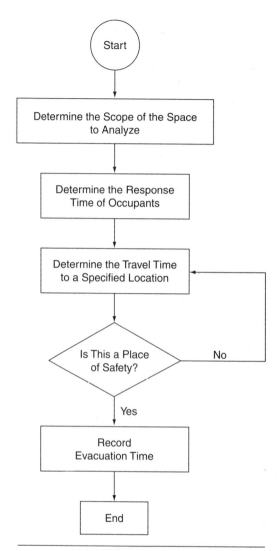

FIGURE 10-6   Methodology for Estimating Evacuation Time

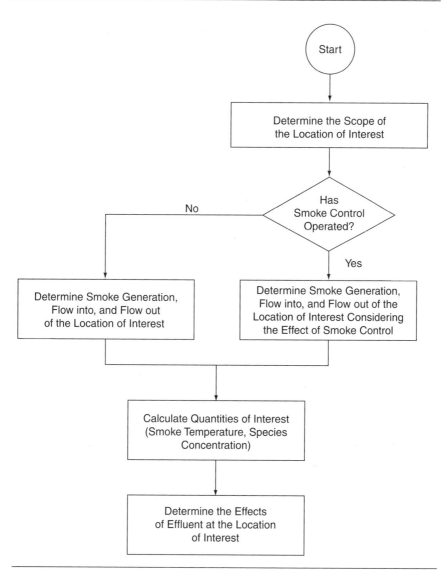

FIGURE 10-7   Methodology for Evaluation the Achievement of Smoke Development Performance Criteria

10.5 Accounting for Known Variations and Unknown Effects (Uncertainty Analysis)

10.5.1 Overview

10.5.1.1   The engineering design process must provide a level of assurance that the designed system or component achieves its performance criteria for the design fire scenarios. The analysis must account for expected variations in materials, components, demands, performance, and occupant characteristics. In prescriptive-based code designs, an unstated excess capacity is used to address variations. (The required design might actually perform better than necessary.) Prescriptive-based code designs with an engineering basis could prescribe a minimum safety factor in an attempt to compensate for unknown variables. This safety factor is derived from either practical experience or estimates of appropriate conservatism. The safety factor commonly applied in a structural stress analysis is an example.

10.5.1.2   For performance-based designs, an allowance must be included to account for unknowns and variations and to provide a level of confidence in the final design. This allowance could be based on historically derived safety factors, an uncertainty analysis, or analysis margins. Each of these techniques is described in the sections that follow.

10.5.1.3   Assumptions, limitations in calculation procedures, and variability in actual versus evaluated scenarios result in uncertainty. Therefore, including explicit uncertainty or safety factors in deterministic-based system-performance evaluations might be appropriate. However, unnecessary or excessive use of safety factors should be avoided if the basic assumptions and calculation procedures are known or have been demonstrated to be highly conservative.

10.5.1.4   Details on available computer models might not allow explicit evaluation of uncertainty. Conservative approaches to design fire scenarios and performance criteria could be utilized to address uncertainty and safety factors.

10.5.1.5   The engineer, in consultation with other stakeholders, should determine whether it is appropriate to include explicit safety factors within the evaluation, or whether the assumptions and calculation procedures are intrinsically and sufficiently conservative.

10.5.1.6   When safety factors are not used, the engineer should understand not only the theory behind uncertainty or margin analysis but also its application to a complex fire protection engineering design.

10.5.2 Uncertainty in the Engineering Design Process

Performance-based fire protection analysis and design relies on current scientific knowledge and the ability to perform accurate technical predictions. Predictions of the buildup of temperature and combustion products in a building as well as the time required to evacuate the building safely are often made. Therefore, the consideration of several key sources of uncertainty in the design process and resulting predictions is important because uncertainty can take many forms. These key sources are as follows:

- Uncertainties about the science and engineering being used
- Uncertainties about human behaviors during a fire
- Uncertainties about risk perceptions, attitudes, and values

For instance, there can be uncertainty regarding the following issues:

- The physical parameters, such as the ignition source, the flame spread rate, and the heat release rate of furnishings
- The appropriateness of a particular tool for a particular prediction
- Human behavioral response to a fire
- The age or health of people who could be exposed to a fire
- Individual and societal attitudes and values

10.5.2.1 Uncertainties in Science and Engineering   The following should be considered when dealing with scientific and engineering uncertainties:[9]

1. *Theory and Model Uncertainties.* In engineering correlations and fire models, theory uncertainty relates to the accuracy and appropriateness of an equation or correlation to the problem being addressed. Because of the limits in scientific knowledge and computing power, all correlations and calculation procedures make simplifying assumptions. Engineering model predictions are based on correlations (e.g., curve fits to empirical data) and on scientific-based calculations (both manual and computer-based). Both correlations and calculations are approximations of reality. Deviations between reality and the model predictions are considered model and theory uncertainty. The appropriate questions regarding theory and model uncertainty relate to the similarity of the design conditions to those conditions under which the correlation data were taken, and how they relate to the appropriateness of assumptions and limitations inherent in scientific calculations compared to those of the design.

2. *Data and Model Inputs.* Much of the input data relating to material properties, fire growth curves, and species production rates are subject to uncertainty. Using a range of values and not simply a single input data point is often necessary. Determining when a range of values is necessary and how to select appropriate input values is discussed in Appendix G, "Uncertainty Analysis."

3. *Calculation Limitations.* Not only are the assumptions inherent in the calculations important to the appropriateness of the use of a tool, but the boundary conditions used in modeling also have considerable potential impact. For example, for most fire models, different answers result, depending on the control volume selected for modeling and the level of detail of the model. More specifically, when applying computational fluid dynamics (CFD) or other finite difference, finite element, or finite volume discritization methods, the size of the grid used to represent the domain can have a significant effect on the model's results. Also significant to the uncertainty in the model predictions are the index variables used to identify a location in the domain of a model or to make calculations specific to a population or geographic region.

4. *Design Fire Scenario Selection.* Differences between reality and the design fire scenarios that were used to evaluate a trial design could exist. The representativeness of the design fire scenarios and their respective design fires should be evaluated.

10.5.2.2 Uncertainties in Human Behaviors
Uncertainty is associated with the human element in performance-based design, from the perspective of how people react in fires and the ability to predict how future human actions could impact the design conditions.[9]

10.5.2.3 Uncertainties in Risk Perceptions, Attitudes, and Values
Uncertainties in risk perceptions, attitudes, and values involve determining what is important to the stakeholders and to what lengths they will go to provide protection. Because most projects have many stakeholders, such as the building owner, the engineer, the architect, the authority having jurisdiction (AHJ), and the public (users of the building), assigning worth to the usefulness or importance of a perception, attitude, or value and applying that worth to both individual and societal issues is difficult. Uncertainties about risk perceptions, attitudes, and values are often at the center of discussions about how safe is safe enough. Decisions that change if a value, attitude, or risk perception varies must be made explicit in the design. Agreement on these key decisions by all stakeholders is critical to the success of a performance-based design. Chapters 5, 6, and 7 describe how to make values and attitudes explicit in the predictions.

10.5.3 Safety Factors

10.5.3.1 Typically, safety factors are historically derived. If an adequate historical data set exists (i.e., a large number of systems that have performed successfully in mitigating a fire), the overcapacity of each successful system can be estimated. The minimum overcapacity could be the basis for the selection of the safety factor.

10.5.3.2 The use of safety factors to achieve the required excess capacity is best suited for deterministic analyses. For most situations, the deterministic analysis should be completed using nominal values when they are the mean values from experimental results. For some situations, the use of other values (e.g., the maximum number of occupants) could be necessary. The types of values used will depend on how the safety factor was derived.

10.5.4 Classical Uncertainty Analysis

The following factors should be considered when dealing with classical uncertainty analysis:[6]

1. Uncertainty analysis techniques were developed to estimate the expected error and variations that occur during measurement and tests. The primary purposes of these analyses is to predict the pre-experiment expectations (e.g., whether the experiment will provide useful results), estimate the accuracy of an instrumentation system (e.g., whether the instrument will provide acceptable information), and estimate the uncertainty of a resultant (e.g., the confidence interval for a test result).

2. In measurement and testing, uncertainty is classified as random or systematic error.

3. Appendix G describes calculation methods that could be used in a classical uncertainty analysis.

10.5.4.1 The uncertainty prediction can be the basis for the design allowance. If the reliability must be 95 percent, then the predicted value must include an allowance equal to or greater than the uncertainty. If the reliability must be 99 percent, then the predicted value must include an allowance equal to or greater than 1.5 times the uncertainty.[6]

10.5.4.2 It is possible to simplify an uncertainty analysis by determining which variables contribute the most significantly to the overall uncertainty. If some variables have a low effect on the results of the analysis, the effect of these variables on the uncertainty could be neglected.

10.5.4.3   The uncertainties in a performance-based design can be grouped as input uncertainties, construction and use variations, calculation methodology limitations, and unrecognized behaviors.

10.5.4.3.1 Input Uncertainties   The following factors should be considered when dealing with input uncertainties:

1. Ranges of certainty can be established for material properties, failure thresholds (e.g., flashover temperature criteria), and equipment performance expectations.

2. For example, a pump will be expected to flow a specific volume of water at a specific pressure (e.g., 0.20 ± 0.02 m^3/s for a discharge pressure of 800 kPa). Thus, the expected flow could range from 0.18–0.22 m^3/s. Typically, these ranges are reported at 95 percent confidence. ASME PTC 19.1, *Test Uncertainty*[6] provides additional details on reporting uncertainties that could be considered inputs to a performance-based design.

3. Other examples of input data uncertainty include material properties, fire growth curves, and species production rates.

4. When using classical uncertainty analysis, the random uncertainties for widely known and developed parameters (e.g., acceleration of gravity) should be based on the mean standard deviation, $S_{\bar{x}}$. For less well-established values, the random uncertainties should be based on the standard deviation of the known data set or sets.

10.5.4.3.2 Construction and Use Variations   The following factors should be considered when dealing with construction and use variations:

1. Ranges can be established for construction (e.g., construction tolerances), material variations (e.g., accepted variations in performance, dimensions, and density), and operating conditions (e.g., combustible loading and occupant loading).

2. When using classical uncertainty analysis, the random uncertainties for construction and use variations should be based on the standard deviation of the known data set or sets.

10.5.4.4   An alternative to the classical uncertainty analysis is presented in Appendix G.

10.5.5 Analysis Margin

10.5.5.1   The confidence that an analyst has in his or her results will vary depending on many factors. The confidence can be referred to as the *analysis margin.* The higher the margin, the more confidence that the prediction will never be exceeded. (Higher margins also equate to more expensive designs.) Qualitative descriptions of confidence include bounding, sufficiently bounding, and best estimate. Each of these terms is defined in the list that follows.

1. *Best Estimate.* When nominal or average data are used for the analysis, the results are described as best estimate. To assume that the predictions will be low 50 percent of the time and high 50 percent of the time is usually acceptable.

2. *Bounding.* When one or more parameters used for the analysis are set to such an extreme that the results are biased to a conservative result (e.g., if a thermally based performance criterion is specified, the use of the highest observed heat release rate as the energy release of the design fire), the results are described as bounding. The selected parameter set at the extreme must provide the most conservative result relative to the performance criteria.

3. *Sufficiently Bounding.* A result is considered sufficiently bounding when all but one parameter used for an analysis are set to best-estimate values, and the one extreme parameter is set as follows:
   - Values associated with operating expectations (e.g., combustible loading and number of building occupants) should be taken at a minimum of 90 percent of the anticipated situations (i.e., coverage). For example, for fixed stadium seating, the 99, 95, and 90 percent coverages could be considered equal to the number of seats if sellouts are anticipated at a majority of the events.
   - Scientific input values (e.g., peak heat release rate and flashover temperature) should be taken at 95 percent coverage.

10.5.5.2 Sufficiently bounding or bounding results should be used in deterministic and risk binning consequence predictions. Best-estimate results should be used in risk binning frequency and explicit risk method predictions.

10.5.6 Other Evaluation Techniques

Several analysis techniques that could be useful in an evaluation are available. Several of the more useful are summarized in the sections that follow.

10.5.6.1 *Importance Analysis* Importance analysis[10] is a process by which each analysis parameter is assigned a numerical ranking on a relative scale from zero to one. An importance value of zero indicates that the variable has no effect on the uncertainty results. A value of one implies total correlation when all of the uncertainty in the results is caused by the uncertainty of a single parameter. This process is especially useful for demonstrating that the inaccuracy of specific variables does not produce a significant inaccuracy in the results.

10.5.6.2 Sensitivity Analysis

Sensitivity analysis[11] determines how changes in one or more parameters of an analysis change the results and conclusions (i.e., the resultant). This change is accomplished by holding all parameters constant while varying a single parameter. The effect of this variation on the output can then be reported. By testing the responsiveness of the results to variations in the values assigned to different input parameters, sensitivity analysis allows the identification of those input parameters that have the most significant effect on the predicted resultant. A sensitivity analysis does not tell the decision maker the value that should be used, but it shows the impact of using different values. A sensitivity analysis performs the following functions:

- Identifies the dominant variables in an analysis
- Demonstrates the sensitivity of the results to variation in input data

10.5.6.3 Switchover Analysis

Switchover analysis is a process in which one or more inputs is iteratively varied in order to find the values (if any) of the inputs that would cause a strong enough change in the value of the resultant to change the final decision.

10.5.6.4 Parametric Analysis

In parametric analysis, detailed information is obtained about the effect of a particular input on the value of the outcome criterion.

10.5.6.5 Comparative Analysis

Comparative analysis evaluates risks and costs in order to mitigate risk by means of comparison to other similar risks.

10.5.6.6 Expert Elicitation

If hard data do not exist and cannot be created, often an expert elicitation is conducted in order to obtain expert judgment of an uncertain quantity.

Notes

1. ASTM E1355, *Standard Guide for Evaluating Predictive Capability of Fire Models*, American Society for Testing and Materials, Philadelphia, PA, 2002.

2. Report on the Technical Investigation of the Station Nightclub Fire, National Institute of Standards and Technology, NCSTAR2, Gaithersburg, MD, 2005.

3. *Engineering Guide to Fire Risk Assessment*, Society of Fire Protection Engineers, Bethesda, MD.

4. "Preparation Guide for U.S. Department of Energy Nonreactor Nuclear Facility Safety Analysis Reports," Department of Energy, DOE-STD-3009, Germantown, MD, 1994.

5. American National Standards Institute, *U.S. Guide to the Expression of Uncertainty in Measurement*, National Conference of Standards Laboratories, Boulder, CO, 1997.

6. ASME PTC 19.1, *Test Uncertainty: Instruments and Apparatus*, American Society of Mechanical Engineers, New York, 1998.

7. Puchovsky, M., & Quiter, J. "Supplement 7—The Application of Performance-Based Design Concepts for Fire and Life Safety," *Life Safety Code® Handbook*, National Fire Protection Association, Quincy, MA, 2006.

8. Evans, D., & Stroup, D. "Methods to Calculate the Response of Heat and Smoke Detectors Installed Below Large Unobstructed Ceilings," National Institute of Standards and Technology, Gaithersburg, MD, 1985.

9. Morgan, M., & Henrion, M. *Uncertainty: A Guide to Dealing with Uncertainty in Quantitative Risk and Policy Analysis*, Cambridge University Press, New York, 1998.

10. Phillips, W. *Tools for Making Acute Risk Decisions with Chemical Process Applications*, Center for Process Safety, New York, 1995.

11. Phillips, W., et al. "Computer Simulation for Fire Protection Engineering," *The SFPE Handbook of Fire Protection Engineering*, 3rd Edition, National Fire Protection Association, Quincy, MA, 2002.

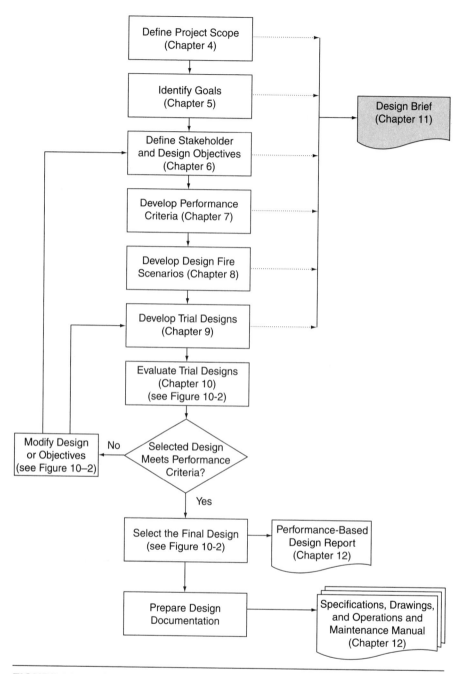

FIGURE 11-1 Overview of the Performance-Based Design Process, Developing a Fire Protection Engineering Design Brief

CHAPTER 11

Developing a Fire Protection Engineering Design Brief

11.1 General

11.1.1 Purpose and Objective   The objective of the Fire Protection Engineering Design Brief (the Brief) is to review and document the architectural proposals, identify potential fire hazards, and define the fire safety problems in qualitative terms that are suitable for detailed analysis and quantification. The fire protection engineering design brief also serves as a useful communication tool to better ensure understanding and agreement with the stakeholders prior to commencing the detailed analysis. Figure 11-1 shows how developing the Brief fits into the overall process of Performance-Based Design.

11.1.2 First Steps   At the beginning of the performance-based analysis and design process, the engineer and other stakeholders should do the following:

1. Agree on the project scope, design intent, and building use.
2. Define and prioritize fire safety objectives and performance criteria and identify the technical bases for the selection of performance criteria.
3. Agree on how the fire safety goals and objectives, as they pertain to the design intent, should be evaluated in accordance with this guide.
4. Determine the implementation of the selected solutions into the project scope and execution.

5. Establish the necessary verification and quality assurance processes, including the technical review processes, needed to ensure compliance with the agreed to solutions.

6. Identify the need for and scope of any technical reviews contemplated during the design process.

The resulting documentation of this process is called the *Fire Protection Engineering Design Brief.*

11.1.3 Responsibility for Developing the Brief   The Fire Protection Engineering Design Brief could be developed by the engineer and presented to other stakeholders for approval or developed collaboratively between the engineer and one or all of the other stakeholders.

11.1.4 Agreeing on a Design Approach   By reaching an agreement on the design approach prior to analysis, the engineer ensures that effort is not expended on any designs or evaluation methods that will not be acceptable to one or more stakeholders.

11.1.5 The Design Sequence   The Fire Protection Engineering Design Brief is usually created after the architectural concept design has been completed. The Fire Protection Engineering Design Brief is created after the engineer has reviewed the project, had initial contact with other stakeholders, and planned a course of action. The Fire Protection Engineering Design Brief documents the agreed upon goals and objectives to the point of concerted analytical analysis and creates a statement of understanding among all the parties involved.

11.1.6 Purpose of the Fire Protection Engineering Design Brief

11.1.6.1   The purpose of the Fire Protection Engineering Design Brief is to document and assist in reaching agreement between the engineer and all stakeholders on the pre-analysis portions of the design prior to commencing the quantitative design and analysis.

11.1.6.2   The Fire Protection Engineering Design Brief documents that all parties involved agree on the performance criteria and the methods that will be employed to evaluate the trial designs. The creation of the Fire Protection Engineering Design Brief will improve communications among stakeholders early in the design in order to prevent any misunderstandings at a point when the resolution might not be easily achieved.

11.1.6.3   The Fire Protection Engineering Design Brief should correlate the performance objectives into quantitative engineering terms that can be incorporated into the design and evaluated during the commissioning and acceptance testing.

11.2 Contents of the Fire Protection Engineering Design Brief

11.2.1 Document Outline

The Fire Protection Engineering Design Brief includes the following items:

- Project scope definition (see Chapter 4)
- Documentation of project participants
- Participants' qualifications
- General project information
- Description of the building and occupant characteristics (see Sections 8.2.3.3 and 8.2.3.4)
- Project goals (see Chapter 5)
- Project objectives (see Chapter 6)
- Performance criteria (see Chapter 7)
- Design fire scenarios (see Section 8.1 through 8.4)
- One or more trial designs (see Chapter 9)
- Critical design assumptions
- Critical design features
- Levels and methods of evaluation (see Section 10.2)
- References
- A record of agreement on the previous items

11.2.2 Documents Included in the Brief   The materials included in the Fire Protection Engineering Design Brief are not necessarily formal submittals, but they are ultimately included in the documentation of the performance-based design. The materials described in the sections that follow should be included.

11.2.2.1 Documentation of Project Participants

11.2.2.1.1 A list identifying all parties participating in the project (i.e., stakeholders) should be created. Identifying the appropriate representatives of the stakeholders, their level of authority, and their ability to prioritize fire safety goals objectives and performance criteria is important. The project management and delivery system should also be identified at this point. Stakeholders who should be documented include, but are not limited to, the following:

- Client/Tenant
- Engineers
- Architects
- Authorities having jurisdiction (AHJs)
- Insurance companies
- Contractors

11.2.2.1.2 The list of participants should include their business addresses, mailing addresses, phone numbers, fax numbers, their levels of authority, and the particular role each person will play in relation to the decision-making process.

11.2.2.1.3 When conflicts of interest between any of the stakeholders exist or may be perceived to exist, a statement should be provided to identify these conflicts and the method the design team intends to utilize to manage these potential conflicts.

11.2.2.2 Documentation of Qualifications

11.2.2.2.1 The design team's qualifications should be formally documented in a "Statement of Design Team Qualifications and Capabilities." The form of this documentation depends on past working relations with the stakeholders and the requirements of state and local law. When presenting the idea of a performance design for the first time to a stakeholder, a resume of key design team members, which discusses educational background, relevant experience with projects of similar scope and magnitude, professional certification and/or licenses and membership on technical committees, might need to be provided. This presentation of qualifications might be the only method a stakeholder has to determine whether he or she will allow the engineer the latitude to prepare a performance design.

11.2.2.2.2   Professional registration such as Professional Engineer (i.e., P.E. or P.Eng.) or Chartered Engineer (i.e., Ch.E.) could be the only requirement to conduct engineering work in a given jurisdiction. However, more qualifications might be necessary to assure the stakeholders that the design team is qualified to perform a performance-based design. These additional qualifications could include resumes of key design team members, descriptions of the design team's experience working on performance-based design projects, and past project references, including facility owners and governing AHJs.

11.2.2.3 General Project Information

After the engineer has demonstrated his or her qualifications for undertaking the performance design, the engineer must reach agreement with other stakeholders on a range of assumptions and methods necessary to perform the calculations for a performance design. These issues include the following:

- *Project Scope.* The project scope clearly defines the borders of the performance design. The scope could include a part of a building, an entire building, or multiple buildings. The project scope will document the engineer's area of responsibility within the overall project.

- *Purpose of Design.* The purpose could be to ensure that the design meets the stakeholder objectives or to evaluate an alternative to a code-specific requirement. For example, most building codes have a section that allows alternative materials or methods to be used in the design of a building. This section could be referenced to show the purpose of the performance-based design.

- *Identification of Objectives and Performance Criteria.* The stakeholder objectives, the design objectives, the performance criteria, and their associated technical bases must be identified. The critical items that will be calculated and presented as part of the performance design must be reviewed with the appropriate stakeholder to gain concurrence on their inclusion in the report.

- *Identification of Fire Scenarios, Trial Designs, and Evaluation Methods.* The selected fire scenarios, one or more trial designs, and the methods intended to evaluate the trial designs against the selected scenarios must be identified. This section will highlight the concurrence that all reasonable scenarios have been considered and that there is stakeholder concurrence of the proposed trial designs. This section should also highlight the AHJ's approval of the selected scenarios and the methods of evaluation.

11.2.2.4 Documentation Methods

The level of sophistication and the methods used to document the performance design vary depending on the scope of the project. The method used to document the design could depend on what the stakeholders want. Regardless of the method used, all the decisions, formal and informal, should be documented in the final report. The following items are examples of this documentation:

- Minutes of meetings and telephone conversations that summarize what factors have been agreed upon
- A formal letter asking for permission to conduct the evaluation in a certain manner, which is subsequently signed and returned or answered formally by stakeholders
- A notation in a log book describing a telephone conversation and a simple understanding of what will be done

11.2.2.5 Revision   The Fire Protection Engineering Design Brief is a dynamic document that can be updated as additional information becomes available (e.g., increased fuel loads, project scope changes, and changes allowing non-ambulatory occupants in which only ambulatory occupants were planned). Upon updating the Fire Protection Engineering Design Brief, all previous documentation should be retained to document design history and development. The Fire Protection Engineering Design Brief may become the basis for initial chapters of the performance-based design report.

11.3 Submittals

11.3.1   Submittals might be made to the stakeholders for their concurrence and to the AHJs for their approval following each step indicated in Section 11.1.2; the completion of several steps; or following the completion of the Fire Protection Engineering Design Brief. It should be recognized, however, that performance-based designs should be ultimately approved as complete designs, not on a piecemeal or partial basis. Although concurrence and approval may occur, in concept, with aspects of a design at each step or following completion of several steps, final concurrence and approval should be based on the complete design.

11.3.2   A submittal schedule can be developed by the engineer to document which stakeholders review which portions of the Fire Protection Engineering Design Brief. The submittal schedule is a tool that follows the progress of the design and obtains any necessary approvals at critical milestones.

11.3.3   The submittal schedule should list each project deliverable and the person(s) who must approve the document. Multiple approvals might be necessary. Not every stakeholder must approve each document. For some projects, the approval order might be of concern. If this is the case, then this information should be agreed upon by the stakeholders in development of the submittal schedule. The submittal schedule should also specify who would get a copy of the final documentation, intermediate deliverables, and the time they are expected.

11.4 Evaluation

Following completion and AHJ's approval and stakeholders' concurrence with the Fire Protection Engineering Design Brief, the engineer will begin the evaluation portion of the design. This portion will include the development of the complete characteristics of the design, quantification of the design fire(s), and evaluation.

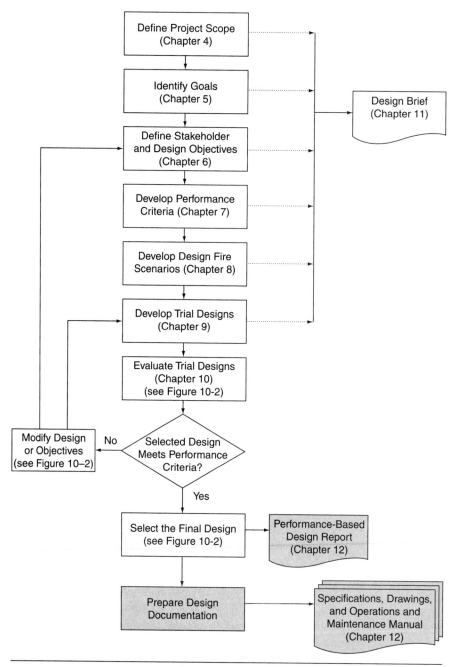

FIGURE 12–1 Overview of the Performance-Based Design Process, Documentation and Specifications

CHAPTER 12

Documentation and Specifications

12.1 General

12.1.1   Proper documentation of a performance design is critical to providing a historical record of the design acceptance, construction process, and methods for addressing future changes. Proper documentation will also assure that all parties involved understand what is necessary for the design implementation, maintenance, and continuity of the fire protection design. If attention to details is maintained in the documentation, then little dispute during approval, construction, startup, and use should occur. Proper documentation increases the likelihood that the design will be accepted by the stakeholders and assures that the design is properly implemented and maintained for the life cycle of the building. The documentation must be presented in a clear manner that accommodates all audiences. Although assumptions could be self-evident, they must be documented to assure agreement by all participants. These documents must be available to all parties throughout the life of the building to assure the continuity of the fire protection features included in the design. Section 12.1.3 lists the types of documents that result from the performance-based design process.

12.1.2   Poor documentation could result in the rejection of an otherwise good design, poor implementation of the design, inadequate system maintenance and reliability, and an incomplete record for future changes or for possible future forensic testing of the design.

12.1.3   The documentation includes the following parts:

- Statement of Design Team Qualifications and Capabilities (see Section 12.2)
- Fire Protection Engineering Design Brief (see Chapter 11)
- Performance-Based Design Report (see Section 12.3)
- Detailed Specifications and Drawings (see Section 12.4)
- Testing Documentation (see Section 12.5)
- Field Change Reports and Documentation (see Section 12.6)
- Verification of Compliance Statement (see Section 12.7)
- Building Operations and Maintenance Manual (see Section 12.8)

12.1.4   Although each documentation part has its own unique requirements, there could be overlapping documentation requirements. Also, each part might be combined with other parts. The documentation of each project will mainly be determined by the requirements of the stakeholders and the unique aspects of the project.

12.1.5   The documentation should be as brief and concise as warranted, provided it adequately reflects all pertinent issues, agreements, assumptions, and analysis. A clear writing style ensures that no important information is lost in the text or is misinterpreted.

All critical design information must be included. For example, if the design is based on a critical fuel load not being exceeded, that fuel load must be maintained throughout the life of the building. If the design is predicated on the proper operation of a suppression system and its reliability, then the maintenance of the system and the proper ways to handle a service interruption must also be included.

12.2 Statement of Design Team Qualifications and Capabilities

It is critical to ensure that the design team possesses appropriate education, training, and experience, as well as appropriate professional certifications and licenses, to design the project. In order to facilitate review of the design teams' qualifications by the interested stakeholders, the design team should submit a "Statement of Design Team Qualifications and Capabilities" to the stakeholders, including the Authorities Having Jurisdiction (AHJs), at the outset of the project for their review and acceptance before significant resources are expended. The Statement of Design Team Qualifications and Capabilities should include the following key information:

- Resumes of key design team members that clearly document:
  - Education
  - Experience
  - Professional certifications and/or licenses
  - Membership on technical committees
- Description of the design team's experience working on performance-based design projects
  - References from past projects
  - Owners
  - AHJs
- Statement of conflicts of interest
  - Identification of conflicts among stakeholders
  - Description of techniques for resolving the identified conflicts

12.3 Performance-Based Design Report

12.3.1   Because of the importance of the design report, it must be a thorough, clear, and unambiguous document. Many stakeholders might review this report, including the AHJ and his or her staff, an appeals board, the building owner, the building insurer, the building operator, a future building purchaser, or a forensic team after a fire in the building has occurred. Because some of these reviewers could have limited technical or fire protection training, the design report should be prepared for a general audience that is representative of the involved stakeholders. When technical terms, concepts, or methods are used, they should be sufficiently explained in such a manner that the document can stand on its own. The report should convey the expected hazards, risks, and system performance over the entire building life cycle (i.e., construction, operation, renovation, and demolition).

12.3.2   Generally, the report could, but need not necessarily, follow the outline in the list that follows. The particular presentation of this information may vary based on the author's personal editorial style. It should include the following items:

- *Project Scope.* The project scope defines the extent of the project (e.g., part of a building or multiple buildings). General information and assumptions relative to the design should be included, such as building characteristics, occupant characteristics, and any existing measures in place.

- *Project Participants.* This is a summary identifying all the stakeholders and their contact information, as well as their roles in the project.
- *Engineer's Capabilities.* This resume and other information present the qualifications of the engineer(s) performing the analysis.
- *Goals and Objectives.* The fire safety goals and objectives agreed between the engineer and other stakeholders should be included in this section. How the stakeholder objectives were developed should be discussed. Also, a description of how the design objectives were developed, including any uncertainty and safety factors, should be included.
- *Performance Criteria.* Each performance criterion should be included in this section. How the performance criteria were developed, including any uncertainty or safety factors, should be discussed.
- *Fire Scenarios and Design Fire Scenarios.* Each fire scenario should be discussed in this section. The selection of design fire scenarios and the basis used to select them should be discussed. The discussion should include the expected conditions under which the design will be valid.
- *Final Design.* The final fire protection systems and controls that were selected from the alternatives and that will be used in the construction of the building should be described with a discussion of how they meet the performance criteria.
- *Evaluation.* The evaluation of the final design should be thoroughly discussed. This discussion should include a description of the evaluation method, the design tools used, and the establishment of uncertainty and safety factors. Any computational tools should be discussed along with the input and output. For some projects, a description of the trial designs that were not selected and the reasons for their rejection could be appropriate.
- *Critical Design Features and Assumptions.* This section includes all the conditions identified as design parameters and assumptions that must be maintained throughout the life cycle of the building in order for the design to function as intended. The design parameters and assumptions should clearly identify their impact on issues related to component and system capability, maintenance, and reliability as well as their interface and interaction with the overall facility design. This identification may also include legal constraints required to be placed in the property deed for the building or other legal construct imposed by jurisdictional authorities.
- *References.* Selected references should be part of the design documentation, especially those that are proprietary or difficult to obtain. Also, those that need to be available to support commissioning and operation and maintenance (O&M) should be provided. The engineer, facility

operators, and AHJ should agree on which references are essential for inclusion in the official project documentation as well as any limitations to their usage and distribution.

12.4 Specifications and Drawings

12.4.1 Role of the Engineer
Preparation of specifications and drawings is subject to the engineer's scope of responsibility and the project management and delivery system employed. The client may elect the extent of the involvement of the engineer. In some cases the client may elect to allow others to develop the additional specifications and drawings. If this is the case, it should be clearly identified in the fire protection design brief. Ideally, the engineer who prepared the fire protection report should develop appropriate specifications and drawings, and if that is not the case, at least review construction documents to determine compliance with the intent and requirements of the fire protection report.

12.4.2 Purpose and Content of Specifications and Drawings
The specifications and drawings must convey to building and system designers and installing contractors how to implement the performance design. Additionally, the specifications and drawings must contain sufficient information to allow the AHJ and other stakeholders to determine compliance with the design parameters. Specifications and drawings could include required sprinkler densities, hydraulic characteristics and spacing requirements; the fire detection and alarm system components and programming; special construction requirements, including means of egress and location of fire-resistive walls, compartmentation; and the coordination of interactive systems. The detailed specifications are the implementation document of the performance-based design report. The specifications are derived from the calculations and results within the report.

12.4.3 Developing a Construction Document
The transformation of the concept design into a construction document is of critical importance. A mistake, such as the transposition of numbers, the dropping of decimal places, or any other inadvertent mistake, could have unintended adverse consequences if the performance design is tested under actual fire conditions.

12.4.4 Revisions
Specifications and design and as-built drawings must be updated upon any facility change to accurately reflect the current conditions in the building. These updated documents will serve as a basis for all future facility changes.

12.4.5 Form of Specifications

12.4.5.1 Attention to detail must be maintained. Master specifications or guide specifications might not be suitable because of the unique features of the performance-based design. Simply referencing existing codes might not be adequate to assure the quality necessary to implement the design. However, portions of prescriptive-based codes and guide specifications could apply. If the fire protection design is predicated on a particular spacing of sprinklers or sprinkler design density, the characteristics and spacing requirements of that sprinkler system must be clearly indicated.

12.4.5.2 The specifications will establish the minimum acceptable characteristics of the fire protection systems and features. Thus, the specifications provide the basis for proper execution of the report recommendations.

12.4.5.3 The specifications should establish the required quality controls necessary to ensure that the fire protection systems and features achieve their intended function.

12.4.5.4 Special inspections, which typically include inspection and testing of the materials, installation, fabrication, erection, or placement of components and connections, may be required during the execution of a performance-based design project. The specifications and drawings should identify the building components and systems that require special inspections as well as any qualifications of special inspectors. The documentation should detail the inspections' scope, frequency, extent, and location in the construction timeline and facility lifecycle.

12.4.6 Detailed Drawings   The detailed drawings graphically represent the results of the performance design. Detailed drawings could include required exit widths, construction features of fire-resistive walls, the location of fire protection devices, and the design of fire protection systems. The detailed drawings create a visual record of the performance design.

12.5 Testing Plan and Documentation

12.5.1 Commissioning of fire protection systems and review of their installation to validate that the installed fire protection systems meet the proposed intent of the design is essential to the level of fire safety provided in the structure. In order for the commissioning to be successful, the performance-based design documents must specify the required commissioning procedures, measurement techniques, and required results. The specifications should also include any acceptable tolerances for each performance metric. The engineer should be involved in the production and review of design documents, review of shop drawings, field inspections, and acceptance testing of the fire protection systems.

12.5.2   During the design process, the engineer should develop a testing plan that includes testing criteria and procedures that meet or exceed the objectives of the stakeholders. It should be presented to the stakeholders for review and consensus concurrence as well as for the AHJ's approval, and the plan and approvals should be included in the design documentation. The engineer should ensure that the stakeholders appreciate the initial and recurring cost implications of the testing and commissioning procedures as part of the performance-based design solution.

12.5.3   Testing plans should include commissioning and acceptance testing and the required frequency of periodic testing to assure system performance. The applicable prescriptive codes should serve as the baseline for the test protocol with rationale submitted for variations from the codes. If the system is unique to the point at which the prescriptive codes provide little useful guidance on commissioning and acceptance testing, the engineer must develop a comprehensive test protocol for review by the stakeholders and approval by the AHJ.

12.5.4   The testing plan should identify appropriate methods and references, if any, on which their proposal for commissioning and acceptance testing is based. The test methods should also indicate the critical path sequence for installation and testing and the role of each party identified to assure that all who participate are aware of the required actions and approximate timeframes.

12.5.5   The testing plan should thoroughly describe the pass/fail criteria that will be applied during commissioning and testing. These criteria should have a foundation on testing procedures established in prescriptive-based codes and standards. Specialized criteria and test methods are not discouraged; however, their development may necessitate the involvement of the engineers responsible for the design and project as well as the AHJ. All criteria should be presented by the engineer to the AHJ for review and approval. A procedure should be identified during design to identify how overly restrictive, inappropriate, or outdated criteria are changed during the life cycle of the facility. This procedure should identify the necessary involvement of the engineer as well as the documentation and rationale that needs to be provided to the AHJ for its review and consideration. It is critical that this procedure be well identified and documented prior to the discovery of a conflict or problem during commissioning or subsequent system testing and inspection.

12.5.6   The engineer should be involved in the documentation of the commissioning and acceptance testing and reporting to the stakeholders and AHJ that all systems and components have been installed and are operational within the tolerances the engineer established. To ensure accurate documentation and reporting, the engineer must be promptly presented with sufficiently clear and complete acceptance test and commissioning data. If not managed at the time of discovery, a failure to address either a deficiency or criteria failure can result in significant future stress and hardship.

12.5.7   The specifications, specifically the sections detailing commissioning procedures and methodology and acceptance criteria, should be presented to the AHJs for their approval prior to final acceptance testing. The arrangements for commissioning and witnessing the final acceptance testing of the systems should be identified and concurred upon by all stakeholders during the design process.

12.5.8   All documentation of commissioning, acceptance and periodic testing, and inspection criteria and results should be maintained with the building records. The criteria should be updated, as necessary, to reflect any changes in the building.

12.6 Field Change Reporting and Documentation

12.6.1   When deviations from the design documents occur, the engineer must be notified so that evaluation, assessment, and reporting of the deviations can be accomplished. The procedure for identifying and documenting field changes and deviations should be established prior to commencing construction. Due to the interdependence of building systems and components in a performance-based design, construction team members should have limited discretion to evaluate and accept or reject deviations without the involvement of the engineer. All deviations that exceed the predetermined design tolerances must be identified and evaluated in the context of the overall performance based design.

12.6.2   The evaluation and assessment may be qualitative, such as comparing the properties and performance of the specified product to those of the product actually provided. The assessment should occur in the context of the overall design and should evaluate the effect of the deviations on other systems. If the assessment reveals that the deviation exceeds the predetermined design tolerances, the assessment will require that the engineer revisit the original engineering analysis and revise key assumptions or calculations. The reporting should incorporate all deviations into the necessary design documentation, based on the impact of the deviation. Specifically, any impact the deviation has on the commissioning and testing procedures should be identified and incorporated in the commissioning and testing plans.

12.6.3 The engineer should notify the AHJ of any deviations from the approved performance-based design. The procedures and time frames for notification should be established prior to the start of construction. When notifying the AHJ, the engineer should identify the scope and reason for the deviation, as well as the engineer's assessment of the deviation's impact on the overall performance-based design. The AHJ should also be involved in any deviation from an agreed upon commissioning and acceptance testing criteria or plan. All deviations should be approved by the AHJ and those approvals of the modified commissioning and acceptance testing plan should be documented.

12.6.4 Upon evaluation, approval, and documentation of field changes and deviations, the engineer should notify all inspectors and provide direction to construction team members as the resolution of the proposed deviation.

12.7 Verification of Compliance

12.7.1 The Verification of Compliance statement certifies that all performance and prescriptive code provisions have been met and should be based on inspection and commissioning reports as well as first-hand observation throughout the construction process. In preparation of the Verification of Compliance documentation the engineer should identify any field changes made during construction, ensure they have been reviewed by the engineer and stakeholders, approved by the AHJ, and properly included in the project documentation.

12.7.2 To ensure continuous compliance throughout the life cycle of the facility, the engineer should include provisions in the Verification of Compliance documentation that detail a process by which the facility may be assessed and monitored for change and a procedure for addressing those changes to ensure continual compliance. A quality control checklist is an example of a useful tool that an inspection team could utilize to identify changes in facility fire safety systems, facility usage, and tenant characteristics and operations.

12.8 Operations and Maintenance Manual

12.8.1   The fire protection operations and maintenance manual clearly states the requirements of the building operator to ensure that the components of the performance design are in place and operating properly. The O&M manual also describes the commissioning requirements and the interaction of the different systems interfaces. All subsystems and associated inspection and testing regimes and schedules are created and acceptable results are identified. Of primary concern is the documentation of the proper function of subsystem interactions. Although some systems might be tested and inspected individually, the interconnections between systems should be periodically tested. This testing includes elevator recall, air handler shutdowns and smoke control activation, and locking door releases. The documentation can be enhanced by including forms for documenting the performance and results of system testing and maintenance directly within the O&M manual.

12.8.2   The O&M manual also gives instructions to the building operator on boundary conditions and restrictions placed on building operations. These limitations are based on the engineer's assumptions during design and analysis. These limiting factors could include critical fuel load, sprinkler design requirements, building use and occupancy, and reliability and maintenance of systems. The design components that are critical to the achievement of the goals must be maintained and a maintenance plan for those components must be developed and documented.

12.8.3   Part of the O&M manual will be used to communicate to tenants and occupants the boundary conditions and limitations and detail the tenants' responsibilities to operate the facility within those limits. This part might also be used as a guide for review and evaluation of renovations and changes within a building that are made or desired by the tenants. It may state a range of building renovations that are permissible within the bounding conditions of the analysis and detail those that need the involvement of the engineer. This part of the document should clearly define a procedure for review and evaluation of all changes within the building to ensure that they are accurately incorporated into the facility documentation.

12.8.4   The O&M manual can be used to document agreements with the stakeholders. These agreements could include inspection frequencies, inspector qualifications, a fee structure for unique AHJ inspections, or a method for selecting a third-party inspection service

12.8.5   The O&M manual should include a statement highlighting the fact that actions might need to be taken if a fire protection system is impaired or removed from service. The selection of compensatory measures could depend on the magnitude and duration of the impairment, such as posting a fire watch during fire alarm system maintenance or reducing the combustible loading if a sprinkler system is removed from service for an extended period of time. The compensatory actions form an integral part of the overall performance-based design and therefore must be clearly understood and agreed to by all stakeholders. Proper documentation of the compensatory actions is essential so that the building operators can readily implement them in the event of system impairment. Having pre-defined threshold impairment durations and associated compensatory measures provides building staff with clear direction in the event of system impairment and prevents the need to develop appropriate compensatory measures after a system is impaired.

12.8.6 The O&M manual should include an update clause that specifies a procedure for updating the O&M manual upon completion of alterations, modifications, changes, and so on.

CHAPTER 13

Managing Facility Changes

13.1 General

The success of a performance-based design, as measured by its ability to meet the stakeholders' goals and objectives, requires adherence to the design criteria throughout the life cycle of the facility. This life cycle could involve changes in individual stakeholders, including owners, facility tenants, management, and maintenance staff; as well as changes in desired facility configurations and occupancy. It is critical that these changes be managed through recognition and adherence to facility maintenance manuals and established procedures for the approval and documentation of facility usage and configuration alterations.

13.2 Incorporating Existing Documentation

The ability to ensure that facility modifications meet the original design goals and objectives relies directly on the amount and accuracy of existing design and construction documentation as well as facility commissioning, inspection, testing, and maintenance reports. This documentation should be the basis for evaluation of any proposed changes or modifications in the facility.

13.3 Change Evaluation, Analysis, and Documentation

13.3.1 All changes to the building must be addressed, regardless of magnitude or their similarity to previously accepted modifications. However, the manner in which the changes are addressed and the amount and type of documentation vary depending on the amount of deviation from the original design.

13.3.2 The original facility design documentation should identify the bounding conditions of the original design and indicate the latitude within which building changes can be made without need for reanalysis or recommissioning of facility fire safety systems.

13.3.3 If the owner or engineer decides that changes or renovations fall within the latitude of the original design, these changes should be presented to the AHJ as part of the notification and permitting process. These changes should be recorded in all copies of facility documentation, including those held by AHJs, in order to monitor changes within the facility. These changes should also be included in updates of facility documentation. Although the individual change may not exceed the performance requirements of the original design, the cumulative effect of multiple changes, even if they are all within the bounding conditions, may result in a facility eventually exceeding the bounding limitations.

13.3.4 Changes or renovations that fall outside the latitude of the original design require a reanalysis of the entire performance-based design against the original goals and objectives. The reanalysis should follow the steps used to evaluate a new performance-based design. The reanalysis should address the specific change, whether it is a building, system, or subsystem, and should be broad enough in scope to ensure that the interactions with other buildings, systems, or subsystems are not adversely affected. Based on this analysis, the engineer should propose the modifications that need to be incorporated to restore or maintain the level of protection in accordance with the documented goals and of the original performance-based design. After the engineer has determined the modifications that should be implemented, the analysis should be submitted to the AHJ for review and approval. This submittal should include sufficient documentation to identify the original design intent, the scope of the change, and demonstrate how the necessary modifications provide a facility that complies with the original design intent. The ultimately approved solution should be incorporated as an update into the facility design documentation.

13.3.5 If the scope of the facility change is of such magnitude that the requisite level of performance cannot be achieved, it may be necessary to revert to the beginning of the performance-based design process and reassess the entire performance-based design, including the goals and objectives, and evaluate different event scenarios and trial designs. This process should follow the outline for the performance of a new performance-based design. A renovation that requires new goals and objectives should produce a completely new set of performance-based design documents.

Additional Readings

Introduction

This Appendix contains a list of supplementary readings on Performance-Based Fire Protection Engineering and related topics.

Performance-Based Fire Protection Engineering

International Fire Engineering Guidelines, Australian Building Codes Board, Canberra, ACT, Australia, 2005.

ISO TR13887, International Standards Organization, Geneva, 1999.

PD 7974, Parts 0–8, Application of fire safety engineering principles to the design of buildings, British Standards Institute, London, 2002.

Reiss, M. "Global Performance-Based Design: Is It the Solution?" *Proceedings, 1998 Pacific Rim Conference and Second International Conference on Performance-Based Codes and Fire Safety Design Methods*, International Conference of Building Officials, Whittier, CA, 1998.

Computer Fire Models

Custer, R.L.P., and Meacham, B.J. *Introduction to Performance-Based Fire Safety*, National Fire Protection Association, Quincy, MA, 1997.

Engineering Guide—Evaluation of the Computer Fire Model DETACT-QS, Society of Fire Protection Engineers, Bethesda, MD, 2002.

Olenick, Stephen M., and Carpenter, Douglas J. "An Updated International Survey of Computer Models for Fire and Smoke," *Journal of Fire Protection Engineering*, 13 (2), 2003, pp. 87–110.

Walton, W.D., Carpenter, D.J., and Budnick, E.K. "Deterministic Computer Fire Models," *Fire Protection Handbook*, 19th Edition, National Fire Protection Association, Quincy, MA, 2003.

Design Fire Scenarios

Alpert, R., and Ward, E.J. "Evaluation of Unsprinklered Fire Hazards," *Fire Safety Journal*, Vol. 7, 1984, pp. 127–143.

Babrauskas, V. "Heat Release Rates," *The SFPE Handbook of Fire Protection Engineering*, 3rd Edition, National Fire Protection Association, Quincy, MA, 2002.

Babrauskas, V. "Table and Charts," *Fire Protection Handbook*, 19th Edition, National Fire Protection Association, Quincy, MA, 2003.

Babruaskas, V. "Will the Second Item Ignite?" *Fire Safety Journal*, Vol. 4, pp. 281–292.

Babrauskas, V., & Grayson, S.J., eds. *Heat Release in Fires*, Elsevier Applied Science Publishers Ltd, 1992.

Cooper, L.Y. "Compartment Fire-Generated Environment and Smoke Filing," *The SFPE Handbook of Fire Protection Engineering*, 3rd Edition, National Fire Protection Association, Quincy, MA, 2002.

Custer, R.L.P. "Applying Models to Fire Protection Engineering Problems," *Fire Protection Handbook*, 19th edition, National Fire Protection Association, Quincy, MA, 2003.

Custer, R.L.P. "Introduction to the Use of Fire Dynamics in Performance based Design," *Proceedings of the Technical Symposium: Applications of Fire Dynamics*, The Society of Fire Protection Engineers and the University of British Columbia, 10–11 July 1995.

Custer R.L.P., and Meacham, B.J. *Introduction to Performance Based Fire Safety*, National Fire Protection Association, Quincy, MA, 1997.

Drysdale, D.D. *Introduction to Fire Dynamics*, 2nd Edition, Chapters 9 and 10, John Wiley and Sons, 1999.

Drysdale, D.D. "Chemistry and Physics of Fire," *Fire Protection Handbook*, 17th Edition, National Fire Protection Association, Quincy, MA, 1991.

Engineering Guide—Fire Exposures to Structural Elements, Society of Fire Protection Engineers, Bethesda, MD, 2004.

"Fuel Properties and Combustion Data," *The SFPE Handbook of Fire Protection Engineering*, 3rd Edition, National Fire Protection Association, Quincy, MA, 2002.

Gottuk, D.T., and Lattimer, B.Y. "Effect of Combustion Conditions on Species Production," *The SFPE Handbook of Fire Protection Engineering*, 3rd Edition, National Fire Protection Association, Quincy, MA, 2002.

Hartzell, G. "Combustion Products and Their Effect on Life Safety," *Fire Protection Handbook*, 17th Edition, National Fire Protection Association, Quincy, MA, 1991.

Mulholland, G.W. "Smoke Production and Properties," *The SFPE Handbook of Fire Protection Engineering*, 3rd Edition, National Fire Protection Association, Quincy, MA, 2002.

NFPA 72®, *National Fire Alarm Code®*, Appendix B, National Fire Protection Association, Quincy, MA, 2002.

NFPA 204, *Guide for Smoke and Heat Venting*, 2002 edition, National Fire Protection Association, Quincy, MA.

NFPA 921, *Guide for Fire and Explosion Investigation*, 2004 edition, National Fire Protection Association, Quincy, MA.

"Performance-Based Fire Scenarios," Primer #3, National Fire Protection Association, Quincy, MA, 1998.

Quintiere, James. "Fundamentals of Enclosure Fire 'Zone' Models," *Journal of Fire Protection Engineering*, Vol. 1, No. 3, 1989, pp. 99–119.

Tewarson, A. "Generation of Heat and Chemical Compounds in Fires," *The SFPE Handbook of Fire Protection Engineering*, 3rd Edition, National Fire Protection Association, Quincy, MA, 2002.

Fire Barrier Damage and Structural Integrity

Fleishmann, C., and Buchanan, A. "Analytical Methods for Determining Fire Resistance of Concrete Members," *The SFPE Handbook of Fire Protection Engineering*, 3rd Edition, National Fire Protection Association, Quincy, MA, 2002.

Milke, J. "Analytical Methods for Determining Fire Resistance of Steel Members," *The SFPE Handbook of Fire Protection Engineering*, National Fire Protection Association, 3rd Edition, Quincy, MA, 2002.

White, R. "Analytical Methods for Determining Fire Resistance of Timber Members," *The SFPE Handbook of Fire Protection Engineering*, 3rd Edition, National Fire Protection Association, Quincy, MA, 2002.

Fire Spread

Drysdale, D. *An Introduction to Fire Dynamics*, John Wiley and Sons, 2nd Edition, 1999.

Quintiere, J.Q. "Surface Flame Spread," *The SFPE Handbook of Fire Protection Engineering*, 3rd Edition, National Fire Protection Association, Quincy, MA, 2002.

Fire Testing

Babrauskas, V., "The Cone Calorimeter," *The SFPE Handbook of Fire Protection Engineering*, 3rd Edition, National Fire Protection Association, Quincy, MA, 2002.

Babrauskas, V., and Grayson, S.J., eds. *Heat Release in Fires*, Elsevier Applied Science Publishers Ltd, 1992.

ISO 9705: Full Scale Room Test, International Standards Organisation, Geneva, Switzerland 2001.

Janssens, M. "Calorimetry," *The SFPE Handbook of Fire Protection Engineering*, 3rd Edition, National Fire Protection Association, Quincy, MA, 2002.

Goals and Objectives

"Goals, Objectives & Performance Criteria," Primer #1, National Fire Protection Association, Quincy, MA, 1998.

Human Behavior

Bryan, J.L. "Behavioral Response to Fire and Smoke," *The SFPE Handbook of Fire Protection Engineering*, 3rd Edition, National Fire Protection Association, Quincy, MA, 2002.

Engineering Guide—Human Behavior in Fire, Society of Fire Protection Engineers, Bethesda, MD, 2003.

Ignition of Objects (Targets)

Engineering Guide—Piloted Ignition of Solid Materials Under Radiant Exposure, Society of Fire Protection Engineers, Bethesda, MD, 2002.

Kanury, A.M. "Flaming Ignition of Solid Fuels," *The SFPE Handbook of Fire Protection Engineering*, 3rd Edition, National Fire Protection Association, Quincy, MA, 2002.

Tewarson, A. "Generation of Heat and Chemical Compounds in Fires," Chapters 3–4, *The SFPE Handbook of Fire Protection Engineering*, National Fire Protection Association, Quincy, MA, 1995. This reference contains information on ignition of solid materials and tabular data of parameters related to ignition for some common materials.

Occupant Response

Engineering Guide—Human Behavior in Fire. Society of Fire Protection Engineers, Bethesda, MD, 2003.

Proulx, G. "The Time Delay to Start Evacuation: Review of Five Case Studies," *Proceedings of the Fifth International Symposium on Fire Safety Science*, Y. Hasemi, ed., International Association for Fire Safety Science, London, 1997.

People Movement

Engineering Guide—Human Behavior in Fire, Society of Fire Protection Engineers, Bethesda, MD, 2003.

Nelson, H.E., & Mowrer, F.W. "Emergency Movement," *The SFPE Handbook of Fire Protection Engineering*, 3rd Edition, National Fire Protection Association, Quincy, MA, 2002.

Proulx, G. "Movement of People: The Evacuation Timing," *The SFPE Handbook of Fire Protection Engineering*, 3rd Edition, National Fire Protection Association, Quincy, MA, 2002.

Smoke Damage

Tewarson, A. "Generation of Heat and Chemical Compounds in Fires," *The SFPE Handbook of Fire Protection Engineering*, 3rd Edition, National Fire Protection Association, Quincy, MA, 2002.

Thermal Effects

Engineering Guide to Assessing Flame Radiation to External Targets from Liquid Pool Fires, Society of Fire Protection Engineers, Bethesda, MD, 1999.

Engineering Guide to Predicting 1st and 2nd Degree Skin Burns, Society of Fire Protection Engineers, Bethesda, MD, 2000.

Purser, D.A. "Toxicity Assessment of Combustion Products," *The SFPE Handbook of Fire Protection Engineering*, 3rd Edition, National Fire Protection Association, Quincy, MA, 2002.

Toxicity

Purser, D.A. "Toxicity Assessment of Combustion Products," *The SFPE Handbook of Fire Protection Engineering*, 3rd Edition, National Fire Protection Association, Quincy, MA, 2002.

Verification Methods

"Verification Methods," Primer #4, National Fire Protection Association, Quincy, MA, 1998.

Visibility

Bryan, J.L. "Behavioral Response to Fire and Smoke," *The SFPE Handbook of Fire Protection Engineering*, 3rd Edition, National Fire Protection Association, Quincy, MA, 2002.

Drysdale, D. *An Introduction to Fire Dynamics*, John Wiley and Sons, 2nd Edition, 1999.

Mulholland, G.W. "Smoke Production and Properties," *The SFPE Handbook of Fire Protection Engineering*, 3rd Edition, National Fire Protection Association, Quincy, MA, 2002.

Purser, D.A. "Toxicity Assessment of Combustion Products," *The SFPE Handbook of Fire Protection Engineering*, 3rd Edition, National Fire Protection Association, Quincy, MA, 2002.

Sources of Heat Release Rate Data

ASTM E1591, *Standard Guide for Obtaining Data for Deterministic Fire Models*, American Society of Testing and Materials, West Conshohocken, PA, 2000.

Babrauskas, V. "Heat Release Rates," *The SFPE Handbook of Fire Protection Engineering*, 3rd Edition, National Fire Protection Association, Quincy, MA, 2002.

Babrauskas V., Lawson J.R., Walton W.D., and Twilley, W.H. "Upholstered Furniture Heat Release Rates Measured With a Furniture Calorimeter,"

NBSIR 82-2604, National Institute of Standards and Technology, Gaithersburg, MD, 1982.

CIBSE Guide E, *Fire Engineering*, The Chartered Institution of Building Services Engineers, London, 2003.

International Fire Engineering Guidelines, Australian Building Codes Board, Canberra, ACT, Australia, 2005.

NFPA 92B, *Standard for Smoke Management Systems in Malls, Atria, and Large Spaces*, 2005 edition, National Fire Protection Association, Quincy, MA.

NFPA 130, *Standard for Fixed Guideway Transit Systems*, 2003 edition, National Fire Protection Association, Quincy, MA.

PD 7974, Parts 0–8, Application of fire safety engineering principles to the design of buildings, British Standards Institute, London, 2002.

Example of Defining Objectives and Setting Performance Criteria

Introduction

In this example, for compliance with existing regulations, a stakeholder is faced with providing complete automatic sprinkler coverage or providing an alternate design that results in an "equivalent" level of safety. In order to develop a design that provides an "equivalent" level of safety, one must do the following:

1. Understand the context of the requirement (establish boundary conditions).
2. Quantify the level of safety provided by the regulatory requirement (in a means acceptable to the stakeholders).
3. Develop (an) alternate design(s).
4. Quantify the level of safety provided by the alternate design(s).
5. Compare the level of safety provided by the alternate design(s) and the regulation-specified design.

In establishing the context of the requirement, one can apply the approach of establishing goals (see Chapter 5).

Establishing Goals

In this example, it is assumed that the requirement for complete automatic sprinkler protection primarily addresses life safety concerns and secondarily addresses property protection concerns.

The goal, therefore, could be to minimize fire-related injuries and prevent undue loss of life. In meeting this goal, it might be assumed that the sprinkler cannot activate fast enough to prevent injury to, or even the death of, a person (or persons) who are in direct contact with the first materials burning. In this case, the objective could be to provide adequate time for those people who are outside the room of fire origin to reach a place of safety without being overcome by the effects of fire and fire effluents. (For the purpose of this example, property protection goals and objectives will be ignored. However, in an actual analysis, property protection might have to be considered if it were included in the regulations.)

Developing Stakeholder Objectives from Fire Protection Goals

The assumed life safety objective—to provide adequate time for people outside the room of fire origin to reach a place of safety without being overcome by the effects of fire and fire effluents—can be accepted by the stakeholders as adequately describing the level of safety intended by the regulation, or the assumed objective can be tested by application of probabilistic and/or deterministic engineering analysis to the code-prescribed parameters. For the purpose of this example, it is assumed that the life safety objective has been agreed to as adequately describing the level of safety intended by the regulation.

Further examples of fire protection goals and stakeholder objectives are provided in Table B-1.

At this point, the engineer and the stakeholders have agreed that the stakeholder objective is to provide adequate time for those people who are outside the room of fire origin to reach a place of safety without being overcome by the effects of fire and fire effluents. However, there is not yet agreement as to how this stakeholder objective could be achieved. To achieve this stakeholder objective, specific design objectives are required.

Developing Design Objectives

For this example, one could assume that if the room of fire origin does not flash over, then fire spread beyond the room of fire origin is minimized. Also, if the fire does not spread beyond the room of fire origin, the conditions in the surrounding spaces are likely to remain tenable. Thus, if flashover is prevented, fire spread beyond the room of fire origin is most likely prevented, and untenable conditions outside the room of fire origin are unlikely. In this case, the stakeholder objective will likely be met. Taking these assumptions

TABLE B-1   Example of Fire Protection Goals and Related Stakeholder Objectives

Fire Protection Goal	Stakeholder Objectives
Minimize fire-related injuries and prevent undue loss of life.	Provide adequate time for people who are not intimate with the first materials burning to reach a place of safety without being overcome by the effects of fire and fire effluents.
	Provide adequate time for people who are outside the room or compartment of fire origin to reach a place of safety without being overcome by the effects of fire and fire effluents.
	Provide adequate time for people who are not on the floor of fire origin to reach a place of safety without being overcome by the effects of fire and fire effluents.
Minimize fire-related damage to the building, its contents, and its historical features and attributes.	Limit fire development and spread such that the structural integrity of the building is not threatened.
	Limit fire development and spread to the compartment of fire origin.
	Limit the spread of fire effluents to the floor of fire origin.
	Limit fire spread to the building of fire origin.
	Limit fire-related damage to a maximum of $500,000.
Minimize undue loss of operations and business-related revenue due to fire-related damage.	Limit fire development and spread to the item of fire origin.
	Limit the development and spread of fire such that the maximum fire-related process downtime is no greater than 24 hours.
	Provide appropriate fire protection measures such that fires originating outside of operation-critical equipment do not cause damage to operation-critical equipment.
Limit the environmental impact of fire and fire protection measures.	Prevent groundwater contamination by run-off of toxic materials as a consequence of the fire or of fire suppression activity.
	Minimize air contamination that could result from the combustion of the building and its contents.

to be valid, a design objective for this example could be to prevent flashover in the room of fire origin. Other possible design objectives could include:

1. Minimize the likelihood of fire spread beyond the room of fire origin. In this case, flashover could occur within the room of fire origin so long as the fire is contained to that room.
2. Detect the fire early enough so that occupants of the building can be alerted to the situation and reach a place of safety before the room flashes over.
3. Detect the fire early enough so that the fire brigade (fire department or local brigade) can respond and take action to contain the fire to the room of fire origin.

In each of these cases, a design objective—flashover, resistance to fire spread, fire detection, egress time, and fire brigade response—was identified in terms that can be evaluated in a probabilistic or deterministic manner. This ability to describe design objectives in quantifiable terms is what differentiates design objectives from more qualitative stakeholder objectives. Table B-2 contains additional examples of design objectives.

TABLE B-2   Examples of Stakeholder Objectives, Design Objectives, and Performance Criteria

Fire Protection Goal	*Stakeholder Objective*	*Design Objective*
Minimize fire-related injuries and prevent undue loss of life	Prevent all loss of life outside the room or compartment of fire origin.	Prevent flashover in the room of fire origin.
Minimize fire-related damage to the building, its contents, and its historical features and attributes.	Prevent all significant thermal damage outside the room or compartment of fire origin.	Minimize the likelihood of fire spread beyond the room of fire origin.
Minimize undue loss of operations and business-related revenue due to fire-related damage.	Prevent process downtime that exceeds eight hours.	Limit the smoke exposure to a degree that would not result in unacceptable damage to the target.
Limit environmental impacts of fire and fire protection measures.	Prevent all groundwater contamination by fire suppression water runoff.	Provide a suitable means for capturing fire protection water runoff.

Setting Performance Criteria

Once the design objectives are established, the performance criteria must be set. Concerning the design objective to prevent flashover in the room of origin, various references indicate that flashover can be characterized by an upper gas layer temperature of about 600°C (1100°F) [1,2] and a heat flux at floor level of at least 20 kW/m² (1.8 BTU/ft²/s). However, other references point out that although a range of 500–600°C is most widely used, gas temperatures in the range of 300–650°C have been associated with flashover.[3,4] (This range in gas temperatures is due to a number of factors, including compartment geometry and volume; fuel type, loading, and characteristics; and compartment ventilation. Likewise, different methods for estimating upper layer temperatures yield similar but different results.)

In another example, maintaining egress path tenability could require both sprinklers and smoke management. In this case, the performance criteria could be sprinkler operation before a fire reaches 250 kW and maintenance of a pressure gradient between the egress path and areas containing smoke of 2.5 Pascal (0.01 inches of water) pressure or higher.

If the performance criteria called for "application of the suppression agent before the heat release rate reached 80 watts" (about the heat release rate from a wooden match) in typical office occupancy, the system could be prohibitively expensive. However, in a telecommunications facility, the damage due to corrosive combustion products could already be done by the time a fire reaches 80 watts. In this case, the added costs of materials control and a very early warning air sampling detection could be called for. Table B-3 contains examples of performance criteria.

TABLE B-3   Examples of Stakeholder Objectives, Design Objectives, and Performance Criteria

Fire Protection Goal	*Stakeholder Objective*	*Design Objective*	*Performance Criteria*
Minimize fire-related injuries and prevent undue loss of life.	Prevent all loss of life outside the room or compartment of fire origin.	Prevent flashover in the room of fire origin.	COHb level not to exceed 12 percent. Visibility greater than 7 meters.
Minimize fire-related damage to the building, its contents, and its historical features and attributes.	Prevent all significant thermal damage outside the room or compartment of fire origin.	Minimize the likelihood of fire spread beyond the room of fire origin.	Upper layer temperature not greater than 200°C.
Minimize undue loss of operations and business-related revenue due to fire-related damage.	Prevent process downtime that exceeds eight hours.	Limit the smoke exposure to less than would result in unacceptable damage to the target.	HCl not greater than 5 ppm. Particulate not greater than 0.5 g/m^3.
Limit environmental impacts of fire and fire protection measures.	Prevent all groundwater contamination by fire suppression water runoff.	Provide a suitable means for capturing fire protection water runoff.	Impoundment capacity at least 1.20 times the design discharge.

Developing a Matrix of Goals and Objectives

Table B-4 suggests a framework for developing a matrix that identifies the various stakeholders and their goals and objectives. In some cases, it could be necessary to assign a weight or priority to the goals. Some occupancies place a higher priority on life safety than on other goals (e.g., a hospital versus a warehouse).

TABLE B-4　Matrix for Identifying Stakeholders and Their Goals and Objectives

Stakeholder	Fire Safety Goals (See Chapter 5)	Fire Safety Objectives (See Chapter 6)	Performance Criteria (See Chapter 7)
Building owner			
Building manager			
Design team			
• Authorities having jurisdiction			
– Fire			
– Building			
– Insurance			
– Accreditation agencies			
• Construction team			
– Construction manager			
– General contractor			
– Subcontractors			
• Tenants			
• Building operations and maintenance			
• Fire service			

Notes

1. Drysdale, D. *An Introduction to Fire Dynamics*, 2nd Edition, John Wiley and Sons, New York, 1999.

2. Walton, W., & Thomas, P. "Estimating Temperatures in Compartment Fires," *The SFPE Handbook of Fire Protection Engineering*, 3rd Edition, National Fire Protection Association, Quincy, MA, 2002.

3. General Services Administration, 41 CFR Part 101-6, (FPMR Amendment A-52), *Federal Register*, Vol. 59, No. 210, 1 November 1994.

4. *NFPA's Future in Performance-Based Codes and Standards*, National Fire Protection Association, Quincy, MA, 1995.

Use of Statistical Data to Choose Likely Fire Scenarios

Introduction

Using statistical data to choose likely fire scenarios can be challenging. Judgment is involved in selecting the categories that define alternative fire scenarios.

Choosing an Appropriate Scenario

One of the first difficulties faced by an analyst who is selecting a fire scenario is that the dimensions and factors used to code and describe historical fires in available databases are not always the same dimensions and factors that are required as input data for a fire hazard analysis model. A translation is required and every translation involves an assumed or demonstrated relationship between fire experience data characteristics and desired input data characteristics. It is essential that these relationships be substantiated as much as possible.

For example, it might not be valid to assume that all arson fires are fast or severe fires (i.e., have a steeply rising rate of heat release or a high peak rate of heat release). Most arson fires do not involve the use of accelerants and are started by juveniles, not by individuals with a sophisticated knowledge of fire. For fire scenario purposes in a fire hazard analysis, the typical arson fire could behave like an ordinary trash fire.[1] By contrast, it could be valid to assume that all fires starting with ignition of flammable liquids, whether accidental or deliberate, show the heat release rate curves associated with those products.

A second difficulty faced by an analyst who is trying to select likely fire scenarios is that the analyst could want to identify fire scenarios that collectively account for a large share, preferably most, of the relevant fires. However, fire hazard analysis calculations typically require input data with so many characteristics defined that no one fire scenario can be expected to account for more than a tiny percentage of total fires. In such a situation, the selection of fire scenarios should be done in two stages. The first stage could be partitioning all the fires that can occur into a manageable number of relatively homogeneous fire scenario clusters. A fire scenario class could be a group of similar fire scenarios that are expected or known to yield similar severities when they occur. The second stage consists of selecting a typical fire within the class to represent the fire scenario cluster.

In a typical building, a manageable fire scenario class for analyzing home fires could consist of all fires originating in ordinary combustibles in any room that people normally occupy, i.e., excluding means of egress that people pass through but do not normally stay in and excluding service areas and concealed spaces. In these cases, the representative fire within the cluster could be upholstered furniture fire within a living room. That is not necessarily the most likely fire scenario within the cluster (kitchen fires involving food on a stove are more common, for example), but it is a very common fire scenario that is easier than a stove fire to quantify for analysis purposes, given existing laboratory data, and is probably more typical of the fires in the cluster.

As the examples cited earlier suggest, high-challenge fire scenarios can often be defined in terms of an area of origin and a fire size, both of which are dimensions that can be assessed statistically and used as engineering specifications for an engineering analysis of a building. Other appropriate dimensions to use in defining high-challenge fire scenarios could include time of day, which is an indicator of the status of occupants.

Using Databases to Analyze Patterns

Three major databases are available to analyze patterns in U.S. fire experience: the annual NFPA survey of fire departments; the FEMA/USFA National Fire Incident Reporting System (NFIRS); and the NFPA Fire Incident Data Organization (FIDO). Together, these three databases can provide information that may be a basis for constructing fire scenarios.

Annual NFPA Survey of Fire Departments

The NFPA survey is based on a stratified random sample of roughly 3,000 U.S. fire departments (or roughly one of every ten fire departments in the country). The survey collects the following information that can be useful in fire hazard calculations: the total number of fire incidents, civilian deaths, civilian injuries, and the total estimated property damage (in dollars) for each of the major property-use classes defined by the NFPA 901 standard[1] for fire incident reporting. These totals are analyzed and reported in NFPA's annual study, "Fire Loss in the United States," which traditionally appears in the September/October issue of *NFPA Journal*.

The NFPA survey is stratified by size of population protected to reduce the uncertainty of the final estimate. Small, rural communities protect fewer people per department and are less likely to respond to the survey, so a larger number of small communities must be surveyed to obtain an adequate sample of those fire departments. NFPA also makes follow-up calls to a sample of the smaller fire departments that do not respond to confirm that those that did respond are truly representative of fire departments of their size. On the other hand, large city departments are so few in number and protect such a large proportion of the population that it makes sense to survey all of them. Most respond, resulting in precision for their part of the final estimate.

These methods have been used in the NFPA survey since 1977. Because of the attention paid to how representative and appropriate weighting formulas are for projecting national estimates, the NFPA survey provides a basis for measuring national trends in fire incidents, civilian deaths and injuries, and direct property loss, as well as for determining patterns and trends by community size and major region.

FEMA/USFA's National Fire Incident Reporting System (NFIRS)

The U.S. Federal Emergency Management Agency's Fire Administration (FEMA/USFA) administers and distributes NFIRS, an annual computerized database of fire incidents, with data classified according to a standard format based on NFPA 901. Roughly three-fourths of all states have NFIRS coordinators who receive fire incident data from participating fire departments and combine the data into a database. This data is then transmitted to FEMA/USFA. (To obtain a copy of the NFIRS data tape for a particular year, contact the National Fire Data Center, U.S. Fire Administration, 16825 South Seton Avenue, Emmitsburg, MD 21727-8995, or call 301-447-6771.) Participation by the states and by local fire departments within participating states is voluntary. NFIRS captures roughly one-third to one-half of all U.S. fires each year. A larger proportion of U.S. fire departments are listed as participants in NFIRS, but not all departments provide data every year.

Data Captured by NFIRS   NFIRS provides the most detailed incident information of any reasonably representative national database that is not limited to large fires. NFIRS is the only database capable of addressing national patterns for fires of all sizes by specific property use and specific fire cause. (The NFPA survey separates fewer than twenty of the hundreds of property use categories defined by NFPA 901 and provides no cause-related information except incendiary and suspicious fires.) NFIRS also captures information on the construction type of the involved building, height of building, extent of flame spread and smoke spread, performance of detectors and sprinklers, and victim characteristics. The latter is published in individual casualty reports that accompany the incident reports in an NFIRS file.

One weakness of NFIRS is that its voluntary character produces annual samples of shifting composition. Despite the fact that NFIRS draws on three times as many fire departments as the NFPA survey, the NFPA survey is more suitable as a basis for projecting national estimates because its sample is truly random and is systematically stratified to be representative.

Usefulness of NFIRS   Most analysts use NFIRS to calculate percentages (e.g., the percentage of residential fires that occur in apartments or the percentage of apartment fire deaths that involve discarded cigarettes), which are then combined with NFPA-survey-based totals to produce estimates of numbers of fires, deaths, injuries, and dollar loss for subparts of the fire problem. This is the simplest approach now available to compensate in the area where NFIRS is weak. It has been documented as an analysis method in a 1989 article in *Fire Technology*.[3]

NFPA's Fire Incident Data Organization (FIDO)

NFPA's FIDO is a computerized index and database that provides the most detailed incident information available, short of a full-scale fire investigation. The fires covered are those deemed by NFPA to be of major technical interest. The tracking system that identifies fires for inclusion in FIDO is believed to provide virtually complete coverage of incidents reported to fire departments that involve three or more civilian deaths, one or more fire fighter deaths, or substantial dollar loss (redefined periodically to reflect the effects of inflation and defined since the late 1980s as $5,000,000 or more in direct property damage).

Data Captured by FIDO   FIDO covers fires from 1971 to date, contains information on more than 70,000 fires, and adds about 2,000 fires per year. NFPA learns of fires that could be candidates for FIDO through a newspaper-clipping service, insurers' reports, state fire marshals, NFIRS, responses to the NFPA annual survey, and other sources. Once notified of a candidate fire, NFPA seeks standardized incident information from the responsible fire department and solicits copies of other reports prepared by concerned parties, such as the fire department's own incident report and results of any investigations.

The strength of FIDO is its depth of detail on individual incidents. Coded information that could be captured by FIDO, but never by NFIRS, includes the following: detailed types and performance of built-in systems for detection, suppression, and control of smoke and flame; detailed factors contributing to flame and smoke spread; estimates of time between major events in fire development (e.g., ignition to detection, detection to alarm); reasons for unusual delay at various points; indirect loss and detailed breakdowns of direct loss; and escapes, rescues, and numbers of occupants. Additional uncoded information often is available in the hard-copy files, which are indexed by FIDO for use in research and analysis.

Usefulness of FIDO   FIDO is a resource that could be used with NFIRS-based national estimates in the same manner that NFIRS is used with the NFPA survey to produce national estimates. That is, a FIDO analysis can provide reasonable estimates of how a block of fires, estimated through NFIRS-based national estimates, further subdivides into more detailed categories.

Access to FIDO   Neither FIDO nor any other special fire incident database with detail exceeding that in NFIRS is directly available to analysts outside the organization that maintains the database. It will be necessary to make arrangements with analysts in charge of the database to obtain needed analyses, and at that time, the database analysts can help indicate what analyses are possible with the data.

Working with the Strengths and Weaknesses of Different Databases

No fire database can possibly capture all instances of unwanted fires. Few databases cover fires that are not reported to fire departments. By their nature, fire databases are biased in favor of "failures" rather than "successes." The fire that is controlled so quickly that it does not need to be reported to a fire department is not captured by the databases that cover reported fires. Analyses of the impact of devices and procedures that provide early detection or suppression also need to allow for the phenomenon of missing "success" stories.

There is also the issue of quality control for a database. For databases with limited depth of detail (like the NFPA survey) or limited breadth of coverage (like FIDO, which is primarily devoted to large fires), it is possible to invest considerable effort in ensuring that each report is as complete and accurate as possible. Follow-up calls can be used to fill gaps and check possible odd answers. For a database with the depth and breadth of NFIRS, however, the same level of quality control effort has not been possible. Consequently, NFIRS is missing more entries and has more that are dubious. The trade-off between data quality and data quantity is never easy; an analyst needs to be aware of the strengths and limitations of the sources before conducting an analysis.

Notes

1. Hall, John R., Jr. *Intentional Fires and Arson*, National Fire Protection Association, Quincy, MA, March 2005.

2. NFPA 901, *Standard Classifications for Incident Reporting and Fire Protection Data*, 2006 edition, National Fire Protection Association, Quincy, MA.

3. Hall, J., & Harwood, B. "The National Estimates Approach to U.S. Fire Statistics," *Fire Technology*, Vol. 25, No. 2, 1989, pp. 99–113.

Examples of Identifying Fire Scenarios and Design Fire Scenarios

Introduction

The examples in this Appendix are intended to illustrate concepts presented in Chapter 8, "Developing Design Fire Scenarios."

Fire Scenario

A fire started in a wastepaper basket by a discarded cigarette smolders for several minutes and eventually leads to ignition of the contents and wastebasket in a hospital waiting room. This fire radiates sufficient energy to ignite an adjacent couch constructed of wood and polyurethane foam. The fire grows large enough to ignite an adjacent wooden wardrobe that provides sufficient heat to cause the room to flashover. Most non-staff occupants are non-ambulatory and are not familiar with the exits or evacuation procedures. The staff has been trained with regards to emergency procedures during a fire incident.

Tools

Failure Analysis This example considers the design of a smoke detection system and a failure analysis to identify ways in which the detection system might not perform as expected. Ambient conditions, such as thermal layering, local heat sources, or the air flow generated by the HVAC system, could prevent smoke from reaching the detector. Thermal layering (for instance in a tall space such as an atrium) could be sufficient to prevent an automatic sprinkler from operating with a fire at the first-floor level. Maintenance conditions could also affect the ability of a detection system to perform as expected.

Each of these possibilities can then be considered as part of fire scenarios. If these fire scenarios were used as design fire scenarios, the impact of these possible failures could be considered. If the detection system were used as part of a larger system, such as one designed for smoke management or the discharge of special suppression agents, the impact of these failures might need to be considered. If these failures resulted in a failure to achieve design objectives, these scenarios would identify the need for to develop alternative detection strategies of failure prevention or mitigation techniques.

"What if?" Analysis   In another example, one could consider what happens if a specific door is open during a fire. Several answers could apply, such as the following: "Nothing, because the door connects to an isolated space not connected to the rest of the building"; "One exit will be blocked"; or "The fire will grow dramatically due to ignition of a more flammable fuel array in the adjacent space."

Fire Initiation Frequency

In some applications, the fire initiation frequency might be based on the building floor area. For simplicity in this example, a homogeneous fire frequency has been assumed. Actual fire frequencies could vary in different areas due to occupancy, use, utilities, time of day, and other factors. Table D-1 shows an example of the process of determining the expected fire frequency for a three-story building from a given fire frequency stated on a per floor area basis. In this example, a fire frequency of $0.3/1,000$ fires/m²-yr is used.

TABLE D–1   Fire Initiation Frequency for a Three-Story Building

	Floor Area	Fire Initiation Frequency (Fires/Year)
First floor	1,000	0.30
Second floor	1,000	0.30
Third floor	800	0.24
Total	2,800	0.84

For this example, the fire initiation frequency would be 0.84 fires per year. In developing and interpreting fire frequencies, it is important not to assume any limitations or conditions other than those explicitly stated. In the preceding example, the value 0.84 fires per year is the estimated frequency of a fire of any size. If the value of interest were the frequency of a fire exceeding a defined size or loss threshold—such as the frequency of fires involving at least a $100,000 loss or of fires with flame spread beyond the room of origin—then that must be explicitly stated and the frequency will be lower.

A conditional probability is the likelihood of an event occurring given the occurrence of a prior event. For example, if a fire occurs, what is the conditional probability that the flame will spread beyond the room of origin? For this example, it is assumed that it has been determined by separate analysis that the conditional probability of fire propagation outside the room of fire origin, given the magnitude and location of the fire and the construction and fire protection features of the building, is approximately 0.1. Then the frequency of fires with flame spread beyond the room of origin will be equal to the frequency of fires (of any size) times the conditional probability that a fire will have flame spread beyond the room of origin. In the example, this would be $0.84 \times 0.1 = 0.084$.

In this example, the expectation is that a fire involving two or more rooms could occur every 11.9 years ($1/0.084 \ \text{yr}^{-1}$). In practice, the two-room fire could occur after this period or it could occur next week.

Reliability and Availability

When the overall system failure probability is reported separately, the following method could be used:

$$P_{fail} = 1 - P_A P_R$$

where P_A = probability system is available to operate
        P_R = probability that, if available, system functions as designed

If a given system is specified to have an availability of 1.0 and a reliability of 0.9, then the system is expected to fail 10 percent of the time.

$$P_{fail} \ [1 - (1.0)(0.9)] \cdot 100\% = 0.1 \cdot 100\% = 10\%$$

If the availability is 0.95 and the reliability is 0.9, the system failure probability is the following:

$$P_{fail} \ [1 - (0.95)(0.9)] \cdot 100\% = 0.145 \cdot 100\% = 14.5\%$$

Risk

For this example, it is assumed for a given facility that a $500,000 loss is expected due to a given fire occurring once every 1000 years. For this facility, a monetary expression of the risk could be estimated as follows:

$$R_\$ = C \cdot F = (\$500,000 \text{ per fire}) \left(\frac{1 \text{ fire}}{1000 \text{ year}} \right) = 500 \ \frac{\$}{\text{year}}$$

If a death were to occur in 1 out of 4 of these fires, then the risk to people could be estimated as the following:

$$R_d = C \cdot F = \left(\frac{1 \text{ death}}{4 \text{ fires}} \right) \left(\frac{1 \text{ fire}}{1000 \text{ year}} \right) = 2.5E - 4 \ \frac{\text{deaths}}{\text{year}}$$

If a death were assumed equivalent to a one million-dollar loss, a monetary expression of the total risk for the preceding example could be estimated as follows:

$$R_t = R_\$ + R_d K_d = 500 \ \frac{\$}{\text{year}} + \left(2.5E - 4 \ \frac{\text{deaths}}{\text{year}} \right) \left(\frac{\$1E6}{\text{death}} \right) = 750 \ \frac{\$}{\text{year}}$$

This example illustrates the concept of risk in a very simplified manner. In practice, there will be a range of possible consequences and associated frequencies, as well as social and values decisions that require the input of all stakeholders. In some cases, the social and values decisions could be codified or influenced by persons outside the initial stakeholder group. This complexity is addressed in Chapter 10, "Evaluating Trial Designs."

Implied Risk

Preventing flashover is a fire protection method that has been used to limit the spread of fire. Flashover could be prevented by limiting the heat release rate of objects. One might assume that for a given room, flashover will not occur if the heat release rate (HRR) is below a threshold value. If the design fire scenario is based on a single item with a HRR slightly below this threshold value, then a second item adjacent to the first will cause the flashover prevention strategy to fail. Implicit in the use of a single item as the design fire scenario is the unstated assumption that the likelihood of the two items being put together when a fire occurs is too low to be considered for design purposes.

Risk Analysis

Introduction

This Appendix presents an example three-room scenario to illustrate methods of calculating, expressing, quantifying, and analyzing risk.

Methods of Expressing Risk

Risk can be quantified on the following basis[1]:

$$Risk = \sum Risk_i = \sum \left(Loss_i \cdot F_i \right)$$

Where $Risk_i$ = Risk associated with scenario i
  $Loss_i$ = Loss associated with scenario i
    F_i = Frequency of scenario i occurring

Additionally, reliability of protection measures, i.e., trial designs, can be included on the following basis:

$$Risk = \sum Risk_i = \sum \left[F_i \cdot \left(Loss_i \cdot R_k + \overline{Loss_i} \left(1 - R_k \right) \right) \right]$$

Where $\overline{Loss_i}$ = Loss associated with scenario i if the trial design fails
    R_k = Reliability of trial design

Alternatively, risk can be expressed as the frequency with which a loss will exceed a given threshold (i.e., performance criteria), as follows:

$$Risk = \sum Risk_i = \sum \left[F_i \left(Loss_i > n \right) \right]$$

Where $F_i(Loss_i > n)$ is the frequency with which a loss will exceed the threshold n (i.e., the set n of performance criteria).

Example Event Tree

In classical risk analysis, often the overall risk is obtained from the sum of the risks associated with individual potential scenarios of a specific type (e.g., fire or explosion), as illustrated using a simple three-room example. Figure E-1 shows an event tree for a three-room building that is subdivided as shown.

For this example, the fire initiation frequency, F_i, is assumed to be uniformly distributed across the three rooms and the consequence of a single room loss is $C/3$ (i.e., the consequence of a fire involving all three rooms would be C). If the probability that the fire will be contained in one room is

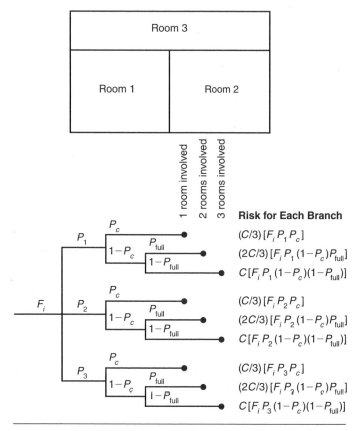

FIGURE E-1   Three-Room Event Tree Risk Example

P_c and the probability that the fire is prevented from propagating to the third is P_f, then the overall risk as shown in Figure E-1 is the following:

$$R = \frac{C}{3}\left[F_iP_1P_c\right] + \frac{2C}{3}\left[F_iP_1\left(1-P_c\right)P_f\right] + C\left[F_iP_1\left(1-P_c\right)\left(1-P_f\right)\right]$$
$$+ \frac{C}{3}\left[F_iP_2P_c\right] + \frac{2C}{3}\left[F_iP_2\left(1-P_c\right)P_f\right] + C\left[F_iP_2\left(1-P_c\right)\left(1-P_f\right)\right]$$
$$+ \frac{C}{3}\left[F_iP_3P_c\right] + \frac{2C}{3}\left[F_iP_3\left(1-P_c\right)P_f\right] + C\left[F_iP_3\left(1-P_c\right)\left(1-P_f\right)\right]$$

where P_1, P_2, and P_3 are the probabilities that a fire will start in room 1, 2, or 3, respectively. This equation can be simplified to the following expression:

$$R = \frac{CF_i}{3}\left[3 - 2P_c - P_f + P_cP_f\right]$$

For this example, P_c and P_f can be interpreted as the success probabilities of the fire barriers. To place these results in context, numeric values will be added. If P_c and P_f are both equal to 0.1 (i.e., fire propagates 9 in 10 times), then the risk is as follows:

$$R = \frac{CF_i}{3}\left[3 - 2\left(0.1\right) - \left(0.1\right) + \left(0.1\right)\left(0.1\right)\right] = 0.90CF_i$$

If P_c and P_f are both equal to 0.9 (i.e., fire propagates 1 in 10 times), then the risk is as follows:

$$R = \frac{CF_i}{3}\left[3 - 2\left(0.9\right) - \left(0.9\right) + \left(0.9\right)\left(0.9\right)\right] = 0.37CF_i$$

If P_c and P_f are set to unity (i.e., fire barriers never fail), then the risk is as follows:

$$R = \frac{CF_i}{3}\left[3 - 2\left(1\right) - \left(1\right) + \left(1\right)\left(1\right)\right] = \frac{CF_i}{3} \approx 0.33CF_i$$

This example is very simplified, however it does suggest how complicated a classical risk analysis can be. For each protective feature, the number of branches (i.e., potential outcomes) in the event tree will increase. This increase is usually geometric.

Risk-Based Calculations

The preceding example also illustrates an important concept in risk-based calculations. The bounding risk for this problem would be CF_i (i.e., complete facility loss). This is the risk if all protective features are assumed to always fail. The risk when the protective features are always assumed to work (i.e., the fire barriers never fail, thus P_c and P_f are set to unity) is the lower bound risk. The potential range for the actual risk is thus bounded between $0.33CF_i$ and CF_i. The better the protection, the closer the risk will approach $0.33CF_i$.

Fire Scenarios Compared to Design Fire Scenarios

The preceding example can also be used to illustrate the difference between fire scenarios and design fire scenarios. The fire scenarios for this example could consider the sequence (e.g., starting in room 1, then going to room 2, and finally to room 3). There are a total of 15 possible paths for the preceding example.

1. Fire starts in Room 1 and is contained in Room 1
2. Fire starts in Room 1 and propagates to Room 2, but not to Room 3
3. Fire starts in Room 1 and propagates to Room 3, but not to Room 2
4. Fire starts in Room 1 and propagates to Room 2 and then to Room 3
5. Fire starts in Room 1 and propagates to Room 3 and then to Room 2
6. Fire starts in Room 2 and is contained in Room 2
7. Fire starts in Room 2 and propagates to Room 1, but not to Room 3
8. Fire starts in Room 2 and propagates to Room 3, but not to Room 1
9. Fire starts in Room 2 and propagates to Room 1 and then to Room 3
10. Fire starts in Room 2 and propagates to Room 3 and then to Room 1
11. Fire starts in Room 3 and is contained in Room 3
12. Fire starts in Room 3 and propagates to Room 1, but not to Room 2
13. Fire starts in Room 3 and propagates to Room 2, but not to Room 1
14. Fire starts in Room 3 and propagates to Room 1 and then to Room 2
15. Fire starts in Room 3 and propagates to Room 2 and then to Room 1

If simultaneous propagation to the second and third rooms were considered a significant threat, there would be 18 scenarios, that is, 18 before considering details such as doors, people, and fire timing.

Analysis of Fire Scenarios

This example demonstrates the level of effort that would be expended if each fire scenario were analyzed. There could be three design fire scenarios for this example: one-, two-, and three-room involvement. For this example (as it was presented) the actual path (sequence of involvement and timing) to this loss is unimportant and thus not part of the design fire scenario. If fire department intervention were credited, then it could be necessary to include a comparison between response time and fire propagation. The intent is to ensure that the design fire scenarios encompass all credible scenarios. Those scenarios that are not encompassed by the selected design fire scenarios would have to be considered an acceptable risk.

Note

1. Custer, R.L.P., & Meacham, B.J. *Introduction to Performance-Based Fire Safety*, Society of Fire Protection Engineers and National Fire Protection Association, Boston, MA, 1997.

Selecting Models or Other Analytical Methods

Editor's Note: Appendix F is adapted from information in the following text:
Custer, R.L.P. and Meacham, B.J. Introduction to Performance-Based Fire
Safety, *National Fire Protection Association, Quincy, MA, 1997.*

Introduction

A wide range of analytical tools is available to the engineer.[1] In selecting a
particular calculation method, it is important to evaluate its predictive capability. Guidance for evaluating the predictive capability of computer fire
models can be found in ASTM E1355.[2] The process of model evaluation is
important in determining the appropriate use, as well as the limitations, for a
particular application. Although a model could be appropriate for one fire
scenario, it could be inappropriate for another.

Sensitivity Analysis

Determining suitability for use also requires an evaluation of the sensitivity of
the given model. Sensitivity analysis is a means of determining the effect of
changes in individual input parameters on the results of a given model. The
analysis can be carried out by holding all but one input variable constant and
systematically studying the effects of that one variable on the predicted result.

Using Models to Predict Outcomes

If there is a high degree of uncertainty about the magnitude or variability of
a given input variable for the design fire or the fire scenario, the model could

be inappropriate if the output is particularly sensitive to that variable. On the other hand, if the given input has little effect on the output, then the tolerance for uncertainty is increased. In most cases, the most significant variable will be the heat release rate history input for the design fire. In some situations, however, heat losses to the compartment boundaries, specification of the physical properties of compartment boundaries, or the size of vent openings could significantly affect the result.

A model's ability to accurately predict outcomes can be assessed by comparison with standard tests or large-scale compartment fire tests. In addition, documented fire experience from actual eyewitness accounts or behavior of materials in actual fires can be used. Another means for evaluation could be comparison of model results with previously published data on full-scale tests in which the specific output parameters being evaluated have been measured. Outcomes such as structural failure, increase of temperature and smoke, available escape time, or the response of detection systems could be used as benchmarks for comparing models to test results.

The process of model selection should also include a review of any limitations placed on the use of the model, either in the applications manual or the supporting technical literature.

General Guidelines for Modeling Analysis

The procedures for conducting a modeling analysis[3] for performance-based design will vary depending on the complexity of the analysis at hand. For example, if the intent is to determine the size of the fire at the time of the sprinkler operation or the length of time required for that operation, the analysis could be performed using DETACT-QS.[4] On the other hand, if the objective is to determine the spacing of smoke detectors for a given design fire scenario that will allow a ten-minute safe egress time from the building in the absence of automatic sprinklers, the analysis becomes more complex.

Developing a Modeling Matrix

One way to organize complex modeling tasks is to prepare an outline or plan indicating the modeling steps that need to be accomplished to arrive at an evaluation of a trial fire protection design for a given design fire scenario. Once the model or models of choice have been selected and documented, a modeling matrix can be developed. The modeling matrix is based on a list of the fire scenarios and design fires to be modeled and a group of trial fire protection designs to be evaluated. The variations included in the matrix can include the presence or absence of specific fire protection systems and location of damage targets, such as occupants or property. Each damage target will be characterized by a performance criterion such as a minimum allowable exposure to heat, smoke, or corrosive agents. In addition, there could be multiple ventilation conditions, such as open and closed doors or HVAC systems on or off.

A full evaluation of a large modeling matrix for a particular design problem could take dozens of runs. To facilitate record keeping, a naming convention should be developed for the data files. The modeling process should be treated as a laboratory experiment in which variables are altered one at a time and a lab notebook is kept. The results should be reviewed as work progresses. Trends can be noted that can help focus the analysis. For example, if the performance criteria (untenable conditions) are reached prior to occupant escape time for small fires with a given detector spacing, it could be unnecessary to run larger fires unless a design involving reduced detector spacing or increased sensitivity is being evaluated.

Computer Modeling

Although each design situation is different, it is often useful to review published work for examples of how other engineers have used analysis and modeling tools. One place to look is in the documentation for specific computer models.[5,6] Frequently, example runs are provided to assist users who are becoming familiar with the software. Studying the manner in which these runs were constructed can be a useful exercise. In addition, various articles have been written describing applications of modeling techniques to a variety of performance-based design problems.

Another source of examples of applications of computer modeling is in the field of fire reconstruction and failure analysis.[7,8,9] A number of studies of actual fires have employed methodologies that might be of use in understanding computer applications.

Limitations of Modeling

There are a number of limitations on the use of correlations and models for the prediction of fire phenomenon. The following is a brief overview of some of the restrictions or assumptions that limit the use of models. The overview is not intended to be exhaustive, and the reader is urged to review the technical documentation and references for models or correlations being used to determine what limitations might be present.

Room Geometry   Most fire models that deal with the prediction of ceiling layer thickness, ceiling jet velocity, or the operation of detection devices are based on the assumption of horizontal smooth ceilings. Thus, calculations with these programs might not model the effect, for example, of beams on the operation of sprinklers. The relative dimensions of compartments are also subject to some restrictions. For example, some models might not be appropriate during early stages of fire growth for rooms with length-to-width ratios greater than 10:1, or for compartments where the height to minimum horizontal distance ratio exceeds one. As such, users are urged to exercise caution when evaluating fires in rooms larger than sizes that have been verified experimentally.[10] In addition, compartment layouts frequently have vent openings (doors and windows) on different wall surfaces. However, computer fire models generally treat the ventilation openings in a compartment as if they were one single opening and do not address any issues that might arise due to the specific location of the given opening.

Interior Finishes   In general, most compartment fire models consider the thermal characteristics of the bounding surfaces of the compartment for the purposes of energy balance calculations. Some published works provide means for calculating flame spread on wall lining materials and for the resulting heat release rate in a compartment.[11,12,13]

Fire Suppression   The effects of non-water-based suppression systems, such as water mist, carbon dioxide, or other gaseous agents, are not modeled. In assessing the effectiveness of these suppression strategies for performance-based design, it is suggested that the engineer review the literature with respect to the performance of the candidate agent in actual fire suppression tests that are similar to the design situation being evaluated. In some instances, it might be valuable to arrange for testing to be conducted to obtain information to adequately model the performance of a system.

Accuracy of Fire Models

The accuracy of a fire model might be assessed by its ability to predict the results of actual experimental data. Assessing models to determine their predictive capability is part of the process described earlier.

A number of published papers compare various fire models and experimental fire data.[14,15,16,17,18,19,20] When reviewing these papers, it is important to understand the implications of the stated outcomes to the specific project under evaluation.

For example, Deal and Beyler[18] compared measured and predicted temperature rise using a variety of different correlations. Their work indicated that some correlations over-predict temperature rise while others tend to under-predict. It is important to understand how variation between predicted and measured values affects the use of correlations and models for performance-based design or evaluation. If one were to select a correlation that over-predicted temperature, it might be said that this would be conservative and, in effect, provide a safety factor. Stated differently, using such a correlation might predict higher than actual temperatures at a given time. The higher than actual temperature could be interpreted to mean that in an actual situation, structural components would be subjected to less than the predicted temperatures, as would unignited combustible materials or even building occupants. If the correlation, however, is used to determine or predict when a sprinkler or detector might operate, it is possible that high temperatures are not conservative, in that the prediction might have the fire protection system operating sooner than it would in the actual situation. On the other hand, under-predicting temperature, for example, could result in higher temperatures at any point in time, thus resulting in greater thermal stresses on structural elements, materials, or occupants within the exposed area.

Nelson and Deal reported on an approach for appraising expected performance of fire models by comparison with actual compartment fire data.[19] In their demonstration of this methodology, Nelson and Deal found that the four models tested provided what they felt were reasonable approximations for the tests being evaluated. Temperature of the upper layer, oxygen concentration, interface height, and flow of products out of a vent from the room were evaluated. The results, however, did indicate that some models tended to under-predict, while others over-predicted actual experimental data.

Other Limitations

Models have other limitations, such as prediction of a uniform temperature throughout the hot layer, and assumption that changes in temperature occur instantaneously throughout the volume of the layer. In addition to the model's documentation, other literature such as *The SFPE Handbook of Fire Protection Engineering* should be consulted to identify these limitations.

Notes

1. Olenick, Stephen M., and Carpenter, Douglas J. "An Updated International Survey of Computer Models for Fire and Smoke," *Journal of Fire Protection Engineering*, 13 (2), 2003, pp. 87–110.

2. ASTM E1355, *Guide for Evaluating the Predictive Capability of Deterministic Fire Models*, American Society for Testing and Materials, Philadelphia, PA, 2005.

3. Custer, R.L.P., and Meacham, B.J. *Introduction to Performance-Based Fire Safety*, National Fire Protection Association, Quincy, MA, 1997.

4. Evans, D., and Stroup, D. "Methods to Calculate the Response of Heat and Smoke Detectors Installed Below Large Unobstructed Ceilings," National Institute of Standards and Technology, Gaithersburg, MD, 1985.

5. Peacock, R.D., Jones, W.W., Bukowski, R.W., and Forney, C.L. *Technical Reference Guide for the HAZARD I Fire Hazard Assessment Method, Version 1.1*, National Institute of Standards and Technology, Gaithersburg, MD, June 1991.

6. Portier, R.W., Peacock, R.D., and Reneke, P.A. *FastLite: Engineering Tools for Estimating Fire Growth and Smoke Transport*, Special Publication 899, National Institute of Standards and Technology, Gaithersburg, MD, April 1996.

7. Nelson, H.E. *An Engineering Analysis of the Early Stages of Fire Development—The Fire at the DuPont Plaza Hotel and Casino—December 31, 1986*, NBSIR87-3560, National Institute of Standards and Technology, Gaithersburg, MD, 1987.

8. Nelson, H.E. "Engineering Analysis of Fire Development in the Hospice of Southern Michigan," *Proceedings of the International Association for Fire Safety Science*, June 13–17, 1988, Tokyo, Japan, Hemisphere Publishing Corporation, New York, New York, 1989, pp. 927–938.

9. Nelson, H.E. *Engineering View of the Fire of May 4, 1988 in the First Interstate Bank Building, Los Angeles, California*, NISTIR89-4061, National Institute of Standards and Technology, Gaithersburg, MD, 1985.

10. Portier, R.W., Reneke, P.E., Jones, W.W., and Peacock, R.D. *A User's Guide for CFAST, Version 1.6*, NISTIR 4985, National Institute of Standards and Technology, Gaithersburg, MD, December 1992.

11. Karlsson, B. "Models for Calculating Flame Spread on Wall Lining Materials and the Resulting Heat Release Rate in a Room," *Fire Safety Journal*, Vol. 23, No. 4, 1994.

12. Mittler, H.E., and Stekler, K.D. *A Model of Flame Spread on Vertical Surfaces*, National Institute of Standards and Technology, Gaithersburg, MD, NISTIR 5619, April 1995.

13. Dembsey, N.A., and Williamson, R.B. "Coupling the Fire Behavior of Contents and Interior Finishes for Performance-Based Fire Codes Evaluation of a Fire Spread Model," *Journal of Fire Protection Engineering*, Vol. 8, No. 3, Society of Fire Protection Engineers, Boston, MA, 1997.

14. Dembsey, N.A., Pagni, P.J., and Williamson, R.B. "Compartment Fire Experimental Data: Comparison to Models," *Proceedings of the International Conference on Fire Research and Engineering*, 10–15 September 1995, Orlando, FL, Society of Fire Protection Engineers, Boston, MA, 1995, pp. 350–355.

15. Wong, Doung, D.Q. "Accuracy of Computer Fire Models: Some Comparisons with Experimental Data with Australia," *Fire Safety Journal*, Vol. 16, No. 6, 1990, pp. 415–431.

16. Peacock, R.F., Davis, S., and Babrauskas, V. "Data for Room Fire Model Comparisons," *Journal of Research of the National Institute of Standards and Technology*, Vol. 96, No. 4, pp. 411–462, Gaithersburg, MD, August 1991.

17. Peacock, R.D., Jones, W.W., and Bukowski, R.W. "Verification of a Model of Fire and Smoke Transport," *Fire Safety Journal*, Vol. 21, No. 2, 1993, pp. 89–129.

18. Deal, S., and Beyler, C.L. "Correlating Pre-flashover Room Fire Temperatures," *Journal of Fire Protection Engineering*, Vol. 2, No. 2, Society of Fire Protection Engineers, Boston, MA, 1990, pp. 33–48.

19. Nelson, H.E., and Deal, S. "Comparing Compartment Fires with Compartment Fire Models," *Proceedings of the 3rd International Symposium of the International Association for Fire Safety Science*, Edinburgh, Scotland, 8–12 July 1991, pp. 719–728.

20. *Engineering Guide—Evaluation of the Computer Fire Model DETACT-QS*, Society of Fire Protection Engineers, Bethesda, MD, 2002.

Uncertainty Analysis

Introduction

For performance-based designs, an understanding of the uncertainties can be important. This appendix provides an overview of the methods, that can be used to evaluate and combine uncertainties. Usually the uncertainty will be dominated by a few key parameters. Significant contributors should be evaluated. A sensitivity analysis as discussed in Section 10.5.6.2 can identify those parameters that are most significant to the uncertainty evaluation.

Steps in an Uncertainty Analysis

In order to determine the best way to treat the uncertainty, several steps are taken:

1. The most significant parameters should be identified.

2. The types of uncertainty (theory, model, etc.) that exist should be identified.

3. It should be determined whether it is crucial to treat the uncertainty quantitatively. The only quantities that need to be treated quantitatively are those for which the uncertainty has scientific significance, that is, the uncertainty is capable of reversing the acceptability of the final solution.

4. The appropriate methodology or tool should be selected for the job.

5. Uncertainty is encoded on crucial variables and propagated throughout the analysis.

Determining the Scientific Significance of an Uncertain Quantity

It could be impossible to treat quantitatively every uncertainty in a complex performance-based design, because the time required and computational complexity would be prohibitive. Fortunately, it is unnecessary to do this. When dealing with uncertainty, one of the most important challenges is to identify and focus on those uncertainties that matter in understanding the fire safety situation and in making decisions about the fire safety tools, methods, and design options.

1. Scientific uncertainty versus statistical uncertainty. Statistically significant refers to a mathematical calculation that verifies that two quantities are in fact the same or different. Scientifically significant refers to whether the difference is large enough to cause a change in the outcome criteria or final decision.

2. Crucial variables. These are defined as those variables whose uncertainties have the potential to change the acceptability of a solution. Several types of sensitivity analysis can be used to determine the scientific significance of an uncertainty and identify the crucial variables. Some of these tools include importance analysis, parametric analysis, and switchover analysis, which are described in Chapter 10.

Selecting the Appropriate Approach or Tool for the Treatment of Uncertainty

An Approach for Scientific Uncertainty (Theory and Model Uncertainties) For an engineering correlation, uncertainties are identified by comparing and contrasting limitations and test conditions to the scenario being evaluated. For engineering calculations, assumptions of the model are compared to the fire scenario being modeled to determine any key differences. For correlations and calculations, comparisons of predictions to real-scale test results are often useful. When available, running various calculations with different models can help to determine an envelope within which the true answer lies.

Data and model inputs are often empirical parameters whose uncertainty can be treated probabilistically. Classical uncertainty analysis, described previously, handles this well.

Domain/Boundary Conditions, Level of Detail of Model To determine how the boundary conditions of a model affect uncertainty, a modeler could conduct multiple runs of a model under various boundary conditions, for example, modeling of a large space in which the boundaries are the entire building versus modeling of a single draft-curtained area. To determine how the level of detail of the model affects uncertainty, one could perform calculations with more than one model. The modeler would run one or two cases with a more detailed model. If widely different results are obtained, the more detailed model should be used.

An Approach for Uncertainties in Human Behaviors, Risk Perceptions, Attitudes, and Values   First, it is important when dealing with these types of uncertainties that all assumptions be made explicit in the analysis. Second, in these areas, one should be especially careful regarding "conservative" assumptions. For example, an assumed soot yield value could be conservative for smoke detector activation and not conservative (in fact the opposite) for life safety. Third, one should perform sensitivity analysis on all human behavioral assumptions, risk perceptions, attitudes, and values to determine assumptions critical to the design outcome. Fourth, it should be made explicit how the results of a calculation change as a function of behavioral changes for these critical assumptions.

Tools for Classical Uncertainty Analysis

Random error is the result of variation or scatter in repeated measurements of a parameter. Random error is typically estimated using the standard deviation of a data set.

$$S = \sqrt{\sum_{k=1}^{N} \frac{\left(X_k - \overline{X}\right)^2}{N-1}}$$

where N is the number of measurements and $\overline{X}$ is the mean of the measurements. If there are multiple sets of measurements, the standard deviation of the sample mean can be used as the random estimate.

$$S_{\overline{X}} = \frac{S_X}{\sqrt{N}}$$

Systematic error, B, is constant for a repeated set of measurements. Based on engineering judgment, systematic error is typically estimated at 95 percent confidence. If the systematic error is not reported, it is usually assumed to be equal to zero.

The total error, U, is the combination of the random error, S, and the systematic error, B. For 95 percent confidence, the equation is as follows:

$$U_{95} = 2\sqrt{\left(\frac{B}{2}\right)^2 + \left(S_{\overline{X}}\right)^2}$$

The parameter will typically be reported as: $\overline{X} \pm U$ (95% confidence).

If multiple parameters are combined to produce a resultant (i.e., a calculation), the uncertainty of the resultant can be estimated by combining the random and systematic uncertainties of each parameter used in the calculations as follows:

$$S_{combined} = \sqrt{\sum_{i=1}^{n} \theta_i S_i^2} \qquad B_{combined} = \sqrt{\sum_{i=1}^{n} \theta_i B_i^2}$$

Where θ is a weighing factor derived from the equation used to produce the resultant.

Guidelines for Peer Review in the Fire Protection Design Process

1.0 General

These guidelines address the initiation, scope, conduct, and report of a peer review of a fire protection engineering design. In these guidelines, peer review is defined as the evaluation of the conceptual and technical soundness of a design by individuals qualified by their education, training, and experience in the same discipline, or a closely related field of science, to judge the worthiness of a design or to assess a design for its likelihood of achieving the intended objectives and the anticipated outcomes. A peer review could be conducted on any or all components of a design, such as the fire protection engineering design brief, conceptual approaches or recommendations, application or interpretation of code requirements, or supporting analyses and calculations.

1.2 Purpose These guidelines provide guidance to members of the Society of Fire Protection Engineers and others in the fire protection engineering community concerning the peer review process of fire protection engineering designs.

1.3 Introduction These guidelines address issues such as when to use a peer reviewer, the choice of reviewer, the scope of the review, the agreements needed, the documentation of the peer review, and other related details. These guidelines describe the decisions that a stakeholder should make in establishing and conducting a peer review. As defined in the *SFPE Engineering Guide* *to Performance-Based Fire Protection*, a stakeholder is an individual or a representative interested in the successful completion of a project.

As performance-based design and other forms of design requiring greater engineering rigor increase, the use of peer review will likely become more prevalent. Peer review is a tool that can be used to help a stakeholder make decisions regarding the suitability of a design. Typically, a peer review is sought by a reviewing authority to provide a second opinion regarding the design's likelihood of achieving the stated objectives. However, other situations may also necessitate a peer review.

Given that the use of a peer review can add time to the critical path of the design process, a stakeholder who wishes the advice of a peer reviewer should begin the process of identifying and contracting for the peer review as early as possible, but no later than at the design review and approval stage when numerous stakeholders are typically involved.

2.0 Scope of a Peer Review

2.1 Overview   The scope of the peer review could be a complete review of the entire documentation, including compliance with applicable codes and standards and the appropriateness of the assumptions, engineering methods, and input data used to support the design. Alternatively, the scope of the peer review could be limited to specific aspects of the design documentation, such as specific models or methods and their associated input data and conclusions drawn from the output data.

Agreement on the scope of the peer review should be achieved between the contracting stakeholder and the peer reviewer. The scope should be explicitly identified at the time of execution of the agreement to undertake the peer review. Any changes to the scope must be agreed to by both the contracting stakeholder and the peer reviewer.

The peer review should be limited to only the technical aspects of the design documentation. The peer review should not evaluate the education, experience, or other personal aspects of the person or company that prepared the design.

The peer review should examine both the internal and external appropriateness of the design. External appropriateness considers whether the correct problems are being solved. Internal appropriateness considers whether the problems are solved correctly.

2.2 Third Party Inspection versus Third Party Review   Some stakeholders may also utilize third parties to undertake inspections of completed installations. As the scope of these inspections is typically related to compliance of the completed installation with the previously reviewed design documents, such inspections are outside the scope of a peer review as covered by these guidelines.

2.3 Details of a Peer Review Whether the scope of the peer review is the complete documentation of a project or some specific aspect of it, the peer reviewer should consider the following details, as appropriate to the design being reviewed:

- Applicable codes, standards, and guides
- Design objectives
- Assumptions made by the designer (e.g., performance criteria, design fire scenarios, and the material properties used in correlations or models)
- Technical approach used by the designer
- Models and methods used to solve the design problem (see Appendix F)
- Input data to the design problem and to the models and methods used
- Appropriateness of recommendations or conclusions with respect to the results of design calculations
- Correctness of the execution of the design approach (e.g., no mathematical errors or errors in interpretation of input or output data)

3.0 Initiation of a Peer Review

3.1 Overview The decision to initiate a peer review is typically made by a project stakeholder whose interest could be financial, environmental, cultural, or related to safety. A peer review is often commissioned by an enforcement official; however, other stakeholders may also commission such a review. This decision usually follows the design development of a project and is occasionally a prescribed part of the design review and approval. A determination to initiate a peer review could be made by a stakeholder during a preliminary project meeting, when he or she is presented with a project design brief or when presented with a complete set of design documents.

3.2 When to Conduct a Peer Review The decision as to whether to conduct a peer review is up to individual stakeholders. The motivation could be a desire to have a better understanding of the quality, completeness, or the scientific bases of the design. The decision to conduct a peer review could also be made by a stakeholder who has resource limitations and wishes to bring in outside assistance to evaluate the fire safety features of the design.

Another possible reason to initiate a peer review could be to provide additional quality assurance for the design.

3.3 Choice of a Peer Reviewer   The importance of a peer reviewer's independence and technical expertise cannot be overemphasized. The peer reviewer should be objective and have no conflict of interest in the project. Any candidate being considered as a peer reviewer should disclose to the contracting stakeholder any conflict of interest or technical bias.

A peer reviewer should have the necessary knowledge and fire protection engineering or fire science expertise to understand and evaluate the design that is being evaluated. For example, a peer reviewer should at least have the necessary knowledge and fire protection engineering experience to prepare an acceptable design that is similar in scope to the design being reviewed. Section 1.2.1 identifies one means to assess the abilities of engineers who are qualified to practice fire protection engineering and prepare acceptable designs. Peer reviewers should be able to demonstrate, through documented education and experience, that they are competent to perform the requested peer review.

3.4 Identification of Agreement to Perform a Peer Review
Prior to commencing a review, the peer reviewer should execute an appropriate agreement with the contracting stakeholder. Once this agreement has been formalized, the contracting stakeholder should notify the design engineer of record, and other appropriate parties, of the initiation of a peer review as required by applicable ordinances, engineering practice acts, canons of ethics, etc. A sample agreement of this type is published by the American Consulting Engineers Council[1] and is available at www.nspe.org. That sample agreement identifies who takes responsibility for design, records retention, confidentiality, dispute resolution, and other related topics.

4.0 Conduct of a Peer Review

4.1 Standard of Care for a Peer Review   Peer reviews should be conducted in accordance with the SFPE Canons of Ethics. Within the agreed-to scope, a peer review should be performed to the same standard of care that would be expected of a responsible designer during the evaluation of trial designs. Section 2.3 of these guidelines identifies the attributes of a performance-based design that should be evaluated during a peer review. However, if a peer-reviewer discovers deficiencies that fall outside of the scope of the review, those deficiencies should be brought to the attention of the contracting stakeholder.

A peer review is often intended to ensure that the public's safety goals or the fire protection goals of other stakeholders are met. Generally, improvement of the design or value engineering is not the purpose of a peer review. The design team will typically accomplish improvement of the design.

4.2 Communications between Peer Reviewer and Designer

Communication between the peer reviewer and the designer can facilitate the peer review. The methods of communication should be understood by all parties.

4.3 Standard of Reasonableness

Peer reviewers should not be influenced by matters of their own design preference, since there will frequently be more than one acceptable solution to a design problem. Technical issues that would not be expected to have a significant effect on the performance of the design should be identified as observations or findings rather than as deficiencies.

4.4 Tools Required for Review

Peer reviewers should have sufficient documentation of the validity of the tools and data that were used in the development of the design. A full evaluation of a design could require that the designer provide the peer reviewer with access to the tools used to develop the design. In such cases, the peer reviewer should respect any confidentiality issues associated with the tools and should use the tools only for conducting the specified peer review. In some peer reviews, it could be necessary to use additional tools and data to perform checks on the results that were obtained during the development of the original design.

Some design and analysis may be carried out using commercial software that is licensed to an individual or company and copies of the software may not be available to the reviewer (e.g. FLUENT, StarCD or ANSYS). There may also be situations in which the reviewer is not familiar with or qualified to use the software. Should this occur, it may be necessary to seek persons with appropriate skills and access to the software to assist in determination of the appropriate use of the software and the accuracy of the input and results. Approval for such arrangements may be needed from the commissioning stakeholder.

4.5 Confidentiality

Normally, the results of a peer review should be communicated only to the contracting stakeholder. At the discretion of the contracting stakeholder, the results may be communicated to the design engineer of record. In some instances, when dictated by professional ethics, communication of the results to the appropriate enforcement officials may be necessary.

4.6 Intellectual Property Rights   During the peer review process, the peer reviewer should treat the information and materials as confidential and with privilege, and should not extract, copy, or reproduce through mechanical, electronic, or other means any or all of the concepts or approaches developed by the design engineer.

5.0 Report of a Peer Review

5.1 Documentation   At the conclusion of a review, the peer reviewer should prepare a written record that identifies the scope of the review and the findings. The report should identify whether, in the peer reviewer's opinion, the design meets the design objectives. The items shown in Section 2.3 of these guidelines should be addressed in the report. Peer reviewers should substantiate any comments on appropriateness by references to published technical documentation.

5.2 Supplemental Information   Resolution of differences in the conclusions between the design team and the peer reviewer may require supplemental technical documentation to resolve the differences. It is important for the designer and the peer reviewer to realize that peer review is only a tool to make an informed decision.

6.0 Additional Information

More information on fire protection engineering, performance-based fire protection design, and peer review in the fire protection design process can be found on the Society of Fire Protection Engineers web page—www.spfe.org.

Note

1. "Standard Form of Agreement between Owner, Designer, and Peer Reviewers for Professional Services for Independent Peer Review." American Consulting Engineers Council, Washington, 1999.

Index

Notes

Notes

Notes